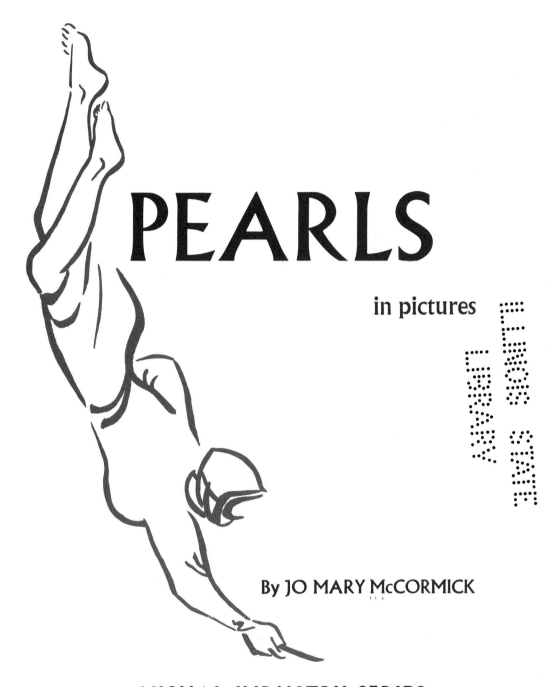

PEARLS

in pictures

By JO MARY McCORMICK

VISUAL INDUSTRY SERIES

STERLING PUBLISHING CO., INC. *New York*

The Oak Tree Press
LONDON AND MELBOURNE

ACKNOWLEDGMENTS

The author and publisher wish to thank the following for their advice and/or photographs: American Museum of Natural History, New York; Australian News and Information Bureau, New York; Mr. Robert Crowningshield; Mr. Victor Ferrante, Cultured Pearl Association of America and Japan, New York; Gem Trade Laboratory; International Public Relations Co., Ltd.; Japan National Tourist Organization, Tokyo; Japan Pearl Exporters Association, Tokyo; Mr. Alan Macnow, Tele-Press Associates, New York; Mastaloni and Sons, Inc., New York; The Melbourne Age, Melbourne; K. Mikimoto and Company, Ltd., New York and Tokyo; Museum of Natural History, New York; National Pearl Research Laboratory, New York; Mr. Mitsuru Okano, Mikimoto Pearl Island, Toba, Japan; Dr. Lucien Pohl; Richelieu Pearls, New York; Tennessee Valley Authority; Van Cleef & Arpels, New York.

Revised and adapted by Jennifer Mellen

A lustrous cultured pearl of the finest quality gleams from an elegant setting. Pearl jewels like this are very costly.

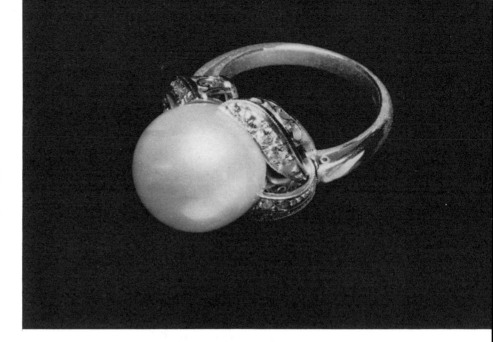

Contents

Wild, uncultivated oysters soon become festooned with seaweed and barnacles. Lying undisturbed at the bottom of the sea, feeding with their shells slightly opened, it is unlikely that these molluscs contain pearls.

"Mobe" pearls are pearls which are attached to the shell of the oyster instead of lying within the oyster's flesh. Mobe pearls are often called blister or half pearls because they are flat on one side. The pearl is sawn out of the shell and used in mountings which conceal the flat back of the pearl. Here, four mobe pearls are used in an opulent necklace.

Natural Pearls

A pearl is a gem created by an oyster in response to an accident of nature. Unlike other gems, unlike diamonds and rubies and emeralds, a pearl is admired not for its sparkle and glitter, but for its soft rich glow. In another way too, a pearl is a unique gem—it can be produced in great quantities through an alliance between man and oyster. It was not always so. In fact, pearls were rare until the opening of the 20th century, when one man, a Japanese noodle-maker, had the imagination and perseverance to change the production of pearls from an accident into an industry.

In this book, you will read about the history of pearls and oysters—natural pearls, imitation pearls and cultured pearls—you will learn about the pearl divers, the people who risked their lives to find pearls; you will discover how oysters secrete the material of which a pearl is formed; you will see how men "farm" pearl oysters, how pearls are graded and sorted, sought and sold, and made into jewelled pieces for adornment.

HOW A PEARL IS FORMED

The oyster, a bivalved mollusc, feeds by opening its shells slightly, allowing the sea water containing its food (plankton) to flow inside its body. Sometimes by an accident of nature tiny grains of sand or other foreign particles are in the sea water and become trapped inside the oyster's shells. The oyster has no use for these rough-surfaced foreign particles, and tries to expel them. But the only way the oyster can do this is by opening and closing its shells. This forces sea water in and out. Often this causes the foreign particle to become even more firmly lodged inside the oyster's body, instead of being washed away.

If a foreign particle gets stuck inside its body, a hapless oyster's only defence is to cover the object with "nacre," the same substance with which it covers the inside of its shells (where the nacre is called mother-of-pearl).

Within three years, during which it deposits layers and layers of nacre round the foreign particle, the oyster builds the jewel which we know as a pearl. It is fortunate for us that the oyster is not a more highly developed animal, for if it were able to expel all foreign particles, we would be deprived of the beauty of this unique gem of the sea.

Since the oyster's normal growth and life-span are not greatly affected by the pearl (or pearls) it may be obliged to produce, it is not certain that the oyster is "irritated" by the foreign particle which forms the core of the pearl, but many scientists think some irritation occurs. It is certain, however, that the shape of the foreign particle and its location within the oyster's body determine the shape of the pearl that will be produced.

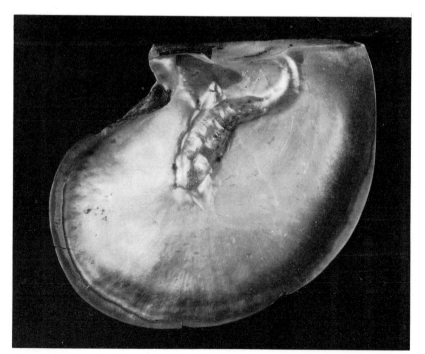

A "cultured" fish! Trapped inside the mollusc's shells, this fish was completely covered with nacre (mother-of-pearl).

Kokichi Mikimoto exhibited this miniature reproduction of a pagoda in 1926. It is decorated with over 200,000 pearls, and took 750 workers more than 6 months to complete.

Early Theories

Men have wondered how pearls are formed since their first acquaintance with them, and many imaginative theories were developed in ancient times. More than 2,000 years ago, it was thought that when the sun was shining brightly the oyster came to the surface of the sea at dawn and opened its shells, whereupon a drop of dew fell inside and became a pearl. The ancient Romans thought pearls were the crystallized tears of the angels, and the ancient Greeks believed the pearl was caused by bolts of lightning piercing the sea. Columbus thought that the dew of the mangrove (a tropical tree that grows at the edge of the water) dropped into the sea and became a pearl. Others thought it was a gallstone created by a diseased oyster.

In 1600, a Dutchman, Anselmus de Boot, noticed the resemblance between the pearl and the inside shell of the oyster. He thought that surplus shell "fluid" developed by the oyster formed the pearl, and this theory came very close to the truth.

7

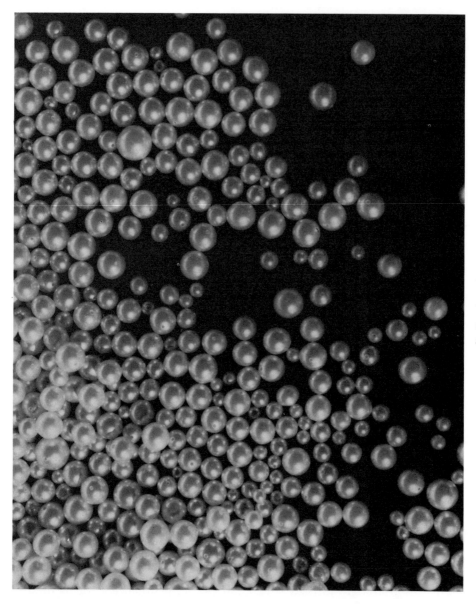

*Variations of shape,
size and hue in
pearls are almost
infinite.*

An Englishman, Sir Edward Hume, presented his theory in 1825. He cut a pearl in half and found a particle of lustrous egg-like material inside. Sir Edward concluded that a pearl was formed when an egg of the oyster died and was not discharged into the sea. At the same time, however, other scientific observers discovered grains of sand in pearls, which gave weight to a theory that had been advanced in 1671 by Francesco Redi, an Italian physician and naturalist. Redi claimed that a grain of sand got into the shell of the oyster and formed the pearl.

The "battle of the pearl nucleus" was waged round the world for more than two centuries before the argument was finally settled: either a particle of organic matter or a grain of sand could be the core about which a pearl is formed.

The Mystery Is Solved

It was 1904 before something quite close to the truth about pearl formation was published: Louis Boutane, a French scientist, announced that if a parasite entered the oyster, settled into the "mantle" (the protective, cloak-like skin layer next to the oyster's shell), and died there, that portion would separate from the rest of the mantle and form a pearl round the parasite.

Finally, in 1907, a Japanese scientist named Tokichi Nishikawa solved the mystery. He announced that when a foreign particle enters the body of an oyster, some of the nacre-secreting cells of the mantle are *carried along with it*. If the foreign object becomes lodged inside the oyster's body, the nacre-secreting cells form a protective sac (called the pearl sac) about the object, and these cells begin to cover the particle with layers of nacre, eventually forming a pearl. It is in the epithelial cells, which form the outermost layer of the mantle, that the nacre is secreted.

Dressed in the centuries-old white costume of her ancestors, this pearl diver ("ama") is resting for a few minutes in between dives. Nowadays the "ama" dive principally for oysters, abalone and other edible seafood and mother-of-pearl shell, not pearls. In olden times the finding of a pearl was a joyous occasion. Proceeds from the sale would supplement the family's income for many years.

9

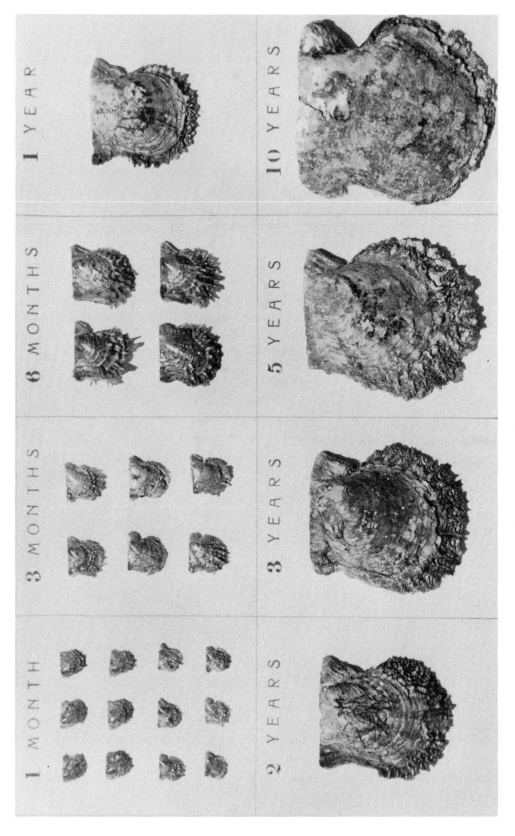

From the time an oyster is a tiny month-old baby (spat), it takes 10 years to become a crusty old-timer 4 or more inches in diameter. The oyster usually is 3 years old before a nucleus can be inserted. Even at full growth, the shell of a Japanese pearl oyster is as fragile as an eggshell.

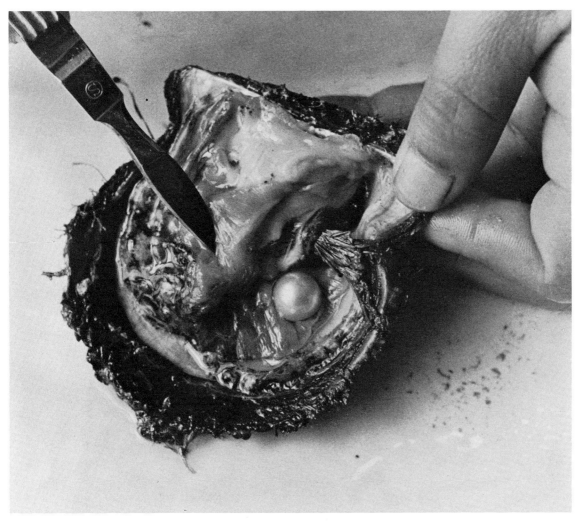

Years of patience and toil are rewarded when the oyster is slit open to reveal a perfect jewel of the sea.

THE PEARL OYSTER

In theory, any bivalved mollusc (soft-bodied water animal living within two shells), such as an oyster, mussel or clam, can produce pearls or mother-of-pearl. Both fresh-water and salt-water molluscs have been found containing pearls, but only certain kinds of oysters (usually not the kind we eat!) produce pearls which are fairly round, beautifully lustrous to look at, and therefore commercially valuable.

Natural pearls often are called "Oriental" pearls, because most of the pearl-bearing species of the oyster come from Japan and the Far East. Among the Japanese pearl oysters are a black-lipped and a golden-lipped variety. Pearls from Japan are generally much smaller than those from the South Pacific and Australia because the Japanese pearl oysters are smaller.

"TOO RICH A PEARL . . ."

The largest natural pearl in the world is the Pearl of Allah, discovered in the shell of a giant clam in the Philippines in 1934. Exactly 9½ inches long and 5½ inches in diameter, it weighs 14 pounds, 2 ounces—a little too large for milady's earlobe. Valued at $3,500,000 (£1,250,000), it is only a collector's item, for unfortunately it possesses little beauty. Several somewhat smaller pearls, such as the mysterious 337-grain *la regente* pearl (stolen in 1792 and reportedly bought by Russian royalty, never to be recovered by France), have a certain odd beauty. But extraordinarily large pearls do not possess the exquisite loveliness of comparatively small but perfect pearls.

Hues

The most valuable pearls are large, perfectly round, and flawless. They range from pale rose to white, but there are many other wonderful hues and shapes. Today the most popular shades are pink, blue, and even silver, in addition to white, black and the very rare iridescent pearl which seems to contain every tint in the rainbow.

Most valuable of all, because it is so rare, is the exciting black pearl, which is actually

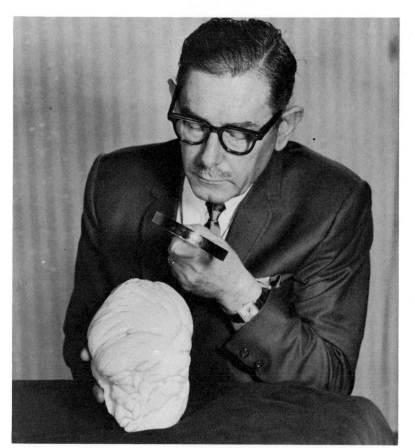

The world's largest natural pearl is the Pearl of Allah. Although unattractive, it is valued for its size and rarity. One of its American owners is examining its lumpy, creased surface.

Black pearls are extremely scarce. Very few —natural or cultured— are found each year. Scientists at the Japan National Research Laboratory have discovered that black pearls can be formed by irradiating pearl oysters with X-rays; however, these often lack lustre. Most black pearls on the market today are dyed, and must be identified as such.

partially green or blue. Perfectly spherical black pearls are almost unknown, but black pearls are very valuable even if they are "baroque" (oddly shaped because of a mis-shapen nucleus or an unusual location within the oyster's body).

The astonishing 220-grain pear-shaped pearl—valued at $16,000,000 (£5,700,000)— which gleams from the peacock throne in Iran, is the most striking example of a golden pearl. Golden pearls signified wealth to the Romans, while green pearls meant happiness, brown were thought to bring wisdom, and white pearls were a symbol of freedom.

Shapes

The shape of a pearl also helps to determine its value. After perfectly round pearls, pear or "drop" shapes are the most desirable, for they can easily be made into earrings or pendants. Next are oval and button shapes, which often result when a nucleus lodges itself near the shell of an oyster and becomes attached to the inner shell during the nacre-secreting process. These are called "blister" pearls, because when they are cut from the oyster they are flat on the side that was attached to the shell. Baroque pearls are the least valuable of all, although they are becoming more and more accepted today as people realize they are not the result of a "sick" or deformed oyster.

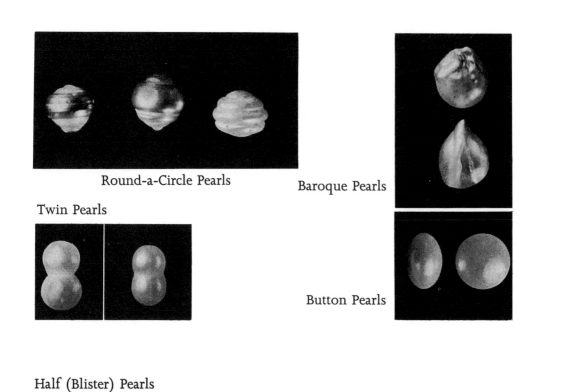

Round-a-Circle Pearls

Baroque Pearls

Twin Pearls

Button Pearls

Half (Blister) Pearls

Three-Quarter Pearls

VIEW FROM BOTTOM   SIDE VIEW

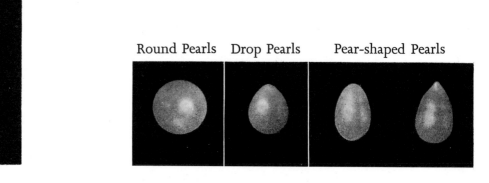

Round Pearls   Drop Pearls   Pear-shaped Pearls

These are some of the pearl shapes used commercially.

The intriguing shapes of large baroque pearls present a challenge to the jewelry designer. Here they are imaginatively used in an elegant pearl bracelet.

Size and Weight

If a pearl is taken from a very young oyster, it is always quite tiny, and is called a "seed" pearl. These pearls are used to decorate fabrics, and are also in demand as jewels for young girls. Mature, more sophisticated women prefer the larger pearls found in 8- to 10-year-old oysters, but these pearls are heavy and very expensive. Pearls are sold according to a special unit of weight called the *momme* or "pearl grain." Four pearl grains equal one carat (200 milligrams) and pearls weighing over 100 grains are so rare they are automatically classed as "treasure."

DIVING FOR NATURAL PEARLS

The demand for pearls has always exceeded the supply. The Roman historian Suetonius even tells us that it was for pearls that Julius Caesar invaded Britain. Perhaps this is true, for after the invasion Caesar presented a breast-plate, set with pink pearls from the Conway River in Wales, to the goddess Venus Genetrix in her temple in Rome.

In ancient times the major sources of pearls were the Persian Gulf, the Red Sea, and Ceylon. Native divers plunged into the sea with little or no protection against the razor-sharp edges of coral beds where they hoped to find pearl-bearing oysters.

Since the divers were paid only for the pearls they found, competition among them was fierce. Even so, few divers ever attained wealth, for they were paid only a fraction of the value of the pearls they did find, while their employers grew plump and wealthy on the profits. Some ruthless employers even ordered their divers to tie heavy rocks about their waists, to carry them to greater depths than they could normally reach—a procedure which considerably shortened the life-spans of the divers.

In the Gulf of Manaar, located between Ceylon and India, pearl fishing usually began in the second week of March, and lasted from 4 to 6 weeks. The pearl divers would not dive without the aid of certain tuneful prayers, sung out from the beach by dervishes or medicine

Many ancient Japanese paintings and woodcuts depict the graceful "ama" at work.

The "ama" of olden times seem to be dancing under water in slow motion as they search the ocean floor.

men. Often one man would chant and perform various rites on the beach, while another accompanied the fleet of 60 to 70 boats.

With 10 divers in each boat, the fleet would set sail before dawn in order to reach the oyster beds by sunrise. Each diver carried a spear of some kind to protect himself from sharks, moray eels, and other enemies of the deep. He would also carry a little net and a heavy stone to which a long cord or rope was attached.

As soon as the boats reached the oyster beds, the fleet captain would sound a signal, whereupon the divers would hurl their heavy stones into the sea. A helper in the boat would grasp the end of the rope tied to the stone, and the diver would follow the rope down into the sea. As quickly as possible the diver would gather as many oysters as he could fit into his net. When his ears began to pound under the tremendous pressure of the sea and he began to feel dizzy, the diver, clutching the bulging net, would tug the rope so his helper could haul him to the surface. With barely a moment to catch his breath, the diver would deposit his booty and swiftly dive down into the sea again. Until sunset signalled the end of the day, he would dive again and again.

The long sail homeward would not bring him rest, either, for those hours would be spent anxiously slitting the "adductor" muscle which holds an oyster's shells together, hoping desperately that inside would be a treasured pearl. But from an average of three tons

17

For many years the pearl divers were unable to search for pearls at great depths because breathing equipment was so primitive. Nowadays diving masks and various types of aqualungs are widely used.

of oysters collected each day by the fleet, perhaps only three or four valuable pearls would be collected, later to be sold at auction.

Pearl fisheries in other areas of the world had varying methods of searching for pearls, depending on local customs. In Japan, the divers along the shores were "ama," women left alone during the day while their fishermen-husbands were off with their boats and nets. The pearls and edible sea creatures they found helped to supplement their husbands' meagre incomes. Everywhere, employers were notoriously slow to improve the conditions under which the divers worked. Many stories have been written about the adventures, the dangers and the tragedies that befell the pearl divers. Their lives were not as tragic as it might seem, however, for each diver had a dream to cling to, and some did find the pearls which are world-famous today.

The Industry Is Threatened

An industry which depends almost completely upon underpaid native workers cannot progress. So, pearl fishing remained relatively primitive while other industries advanced by leaps and bounds. Although some diving equipment was developed during the 19th century, this was only because the supply of oysters was dwindling rapidly and the divers had to search deeper.

Below depths of 70 feet, man needs artificial breathing equipment to survive. Primitive masks made of wood developed into the plastic face coverings used today. Breathing tubes of natural reeds were probably the ancestors of our modern "snorkels." Despite technical advances, as recently as 1890 some divers were still being sent down into the sea equipped with only a dilapidated diving helmet and perhaps an unreliable hand-pump and air hose. But this was not the most important fault of the industry.

Greed and lack of foresight brought on a crucial situation by the middle of the 19th century: oyster beds throughout the world were either completely destroyed or seriously depleted. So many millions of oysters had been carelessly and thoughtlessly wrested from their motherbeds in the search for pearls that the oyster population was simply unable to keep up with the death rate. Pearl oysters were in danger of becoming extinct. Even more serious was the fact that this critical situation seemed to have been discovered too late. No one knew what to do about it until Kokichi Mikimoto began his work in the 1880's.

The Great Barrier Reef of Australia is the home of many Australian pearl oysters.

THE BIRTH OF A NEW INDUSTRY

A noodle-maker turned vegetable peddler, Kokichi Mikimoto was still poverty-stricken at the age of 33 when he saw pearls for the first time at a marine exhibition in Yokohama. With only limited knowledge of the experiments previously carried out, Mikimoto was inspired to make the culture of pearls his life's work. He had waited for this inspiration since the age of 12, when he vowed to become the third richest man in Toba city; modesty forbade a higher aspiration. His incredible persistence, patience, and determination were responsible perhaps more than any other single factor for the development and success of the cultured pearl. But the road from ignorant peddler to "Pearl King" was paved with very rough stones.

The theory which Mikimoto developed was simple but ingenious. He reasoned that if oysters were to survive and produce pearls, they must be protected from extinction. So, he thought, why not cultivate and harvest them? He suggested that oysters be collected and farmed, much as a farmer cultivates his chickens or a shepherd tends his flock. He planned to gather as many oysters as he could find, and set them out in sheltered areas off the coast of Japan where they could thrive in warm, safe waters and multiply. Then he would experiment to discover how to encourage oysters to produce pearls.

It took Mikimoto many months to convince the Japanese government that this was indeed a practical scheme, and many more months to put it into effect. His most difficult task was to convince the villagers in the areas he had chosen that "pearl farming" would be a more profitable enterprise than fishing, the principal occupation of the villagers at that time. This was not an easy task, for it meant the fishermen would have to endure two or three years of financial hardship before they could expect profits. But Mikimoto finally managed to persuade

This scale model of Mount Vernon, George Washington's home, was presented by Mikimoto to the Smithsonian Institution, Washington, D.C., in 1934. More than 20,000 pearls decorate the flag, gleaming courtyard, and mother-of-pearl walls and roof.

Mikimoto had so much respect for George Washington, that when visiting America his first stop in the Washington area was the late President's tomb. Unrolling a long scroll, Mikimoto read aloud a report on the cultured pearl industry to the United States' "Number One ancestor." Startled visitors to the tomb learned that this was in keeping with the Japanese tradition of periodically reporting one's progress to one's ancestors.

the inhabitants of Jinmyo Mura, a tiny hamlet near Ago Bay, to try his plan. In September, 1888, the villagers began to establish the first Mikimoto pearl farm.

A year later Mikimoto's first crop of oysters was harvested, and it yielded enough pearls so that the enterprise could continue. Then a question began to form in his mind while the sowing and harvesting continued year after year: how do pearls come into being in the first place? Mikimoto, together with scientists like Nishikawa, was to answer that question and go on to establish a whole new industry.

The pearl film must be carefully stirred before each dipping. Although the exact composition of the film is a secret, it is known that it contains herring and other iridescent fish scales.

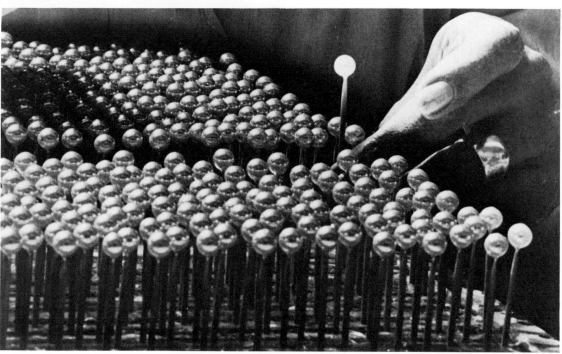

These imitation pearls have been dipped seven times in a special solution, and are now ready to be polished. After the polished pearls are removed from the needle-like holders, they are ready to be strung.

This fanciful wig is made entirely of top quality imitation pearls, as is the more familiar three-strand necklace.

Imitation Pearls

While Mikimoto was busily farming oysters, another branch of the pearl industry began to sprout. This branch eventually "dropped off" and went its separate way, but it did develop initially as part of the pearl industry.

As the shortage of oysters became acute and the demand for pearls increased yearly, prices for pearls began to soar. Businessmen reacted to this development by trying to produce an inexpensive facsimile, or imitation, of the pearl. Unlike cultured pearls, imitation or "simulated" pearls are not related in any way to real pearls, and in fact most of them bear little resemblance to lustrous, shimmering natural pearls. Although some unscrupulous

The plastic beads which will form the "nucleus" of imitation pearls are tumbled in wet powdered pumice (volcanic glass) to remove grinding marks. The smooth spheres are sprayed with water to remove gritty traces before they are dipped in pearl film.

dealers at first tried to sell imitation pearls as real pearls, today sales are strictly regulated. Reputable dealers today must label imitation pearls as such, even though an expert at a glance can distinguish the real and cultured pearls from the imitation.

The first imitation pearls were made in Paris by a rosary maker named Jacquin. The silvery scales of the tiny bleak fish, a relative of the carp, were made into a liquid substance known as *essence d'orient*. This was applied to the inner surface of small glass balls, which were then filled with white wax. Since then many different processes have evolved, and literally millions of imitation pearls are manufactured and sold each year all over the world.

Rolling carts carry trays of simulated pearls from one dipping station to another.

Plastic beads are dipped by hand in various solutions of pearl film. Each dipping increases the value of the simulated pearl.

Quality ranges from the very beautiful "Majorca" pearls made in Spain to cheap, shoddy and peeling white balls made of plastic. Some imitation pearls are made with fine materials such as mother-of-pearl shell, conch shell and coral, but most are made with inexpensive chemicals.

Now imitation pearls are classed with costume jewelry, and by no means does the industry function hand-in-glove with the pearl industry. In fact, pearl dealers and wholesale buyers usually trade either in cultured or imitation pearls, not both.

Imitation pearls constitute a multi-million business today, which did at first compete with cultured pearls, but now that the differences between the products are understood by the general public, the industries are almost as separate as though they dealt in different products, for in a sense, they do. Imitation pearls and cultured or natural pearls are all used as jewelry, but there the resemblance ends.

25

The Emperor of Japan awarded this unique gold-topped staff to Kokichi Mikimoto, the "Pearl King," in recognition of his achievements in the development of the cultured pearl industry.

Of the bulk harvest, usually only 5 to 10 per cent will be pearls of quality.

Some cultured pearls available today have surpassed natural pearls in value. A superb necklace of cultured pearls like this, clasped with precious stones, can cost more than $150,000 (£50,000). While a few jewel shops keep a limited supply of natural (or "Oriental" as they are known in the trade) pearls on hand "for the few people who want them," cultured pearls have almost completely dominated the market.

Cultured Pearls

THE FIRST HALTING STEPS

By 1890, when Mikimoto's oyster beds were cradling hundreds of thousands of pearl oysters, the problem of extinction was well on its way to being solved. The waters that Mikimoto chose along the southern coast of Japan for his pearl farms were ideal for oyster cultivation. The oysters reproduced at a satisfactory rate. At harvest time there were enough natural pearls and marketable by-products (mother-of-pearl shell and edible abalone) and sufficient profits to continue the operation of the farms. In the meantime, the efforts of

27

Mikimoto and other Japanese scientists were concentrated upon finding a way to discover the oyster's secret and encourage the mollusc to produce pearls at man's bidding. Within a few short years the element of chance in pearl production was to be eliminated.

It is difficult to untangle the claims surrounding early Japanese pearl research. But we know that through his knowledge of early Chinese experiments, Mikimoto was able to produce "blister" pearls (half pearls that adhere to the oyster's inner shell) by 1893. The real question was whether a perfectly round pearl could be produced, for the demand for blister pearls was not enough to sustain the industry. So many men were involved in the search in the 1890's for a way to produce round pearls, and competition was so fierce, that historians today find it is nearly impossible to credit any one person with being "the" developer of the round cultured pearl.

Beautiful Ago Bay, on a peninsula south of the city of Nagoya, Japan, is the picturesque home of the Mikimoto pearl farms. This "sea of pearls" is a sheltered inlet, providing the moderate climate and warm currents essential to pearl oysters. The structures on the water are rafts, from which the oysters are suspended in their cages.

Nacre-covered Buddhas were the first cultured pearls. Tin or lead images of Buddha were inserted between the outer skin layer (mantle) and the shell of this fresh-water mollusc, which soon covered them with nacre. Pried from the shell, the pearl-covered Buddhas were sold as religious charms.

BLISTER PEARLS

Production of cultured pearls apparently began in China in about the 13th century. Foreign objects such as tiny images of Buddha (see photograph) were inserted between the mantle and the shell of living oysters, and the oysters were returned to their home in the sea. When the oysters were pried open one or two years later, the Chinese found that the Buddha images were covered with a thin coating of nacre. Such crude pearl-covered images are still sold to devout Buddhists today, but the market now, as then, is not extensive.

Mikimoto adapted this method in his first attempts to produce pearls, and he became the first man to produce semi-spherical, or blister, pearls in quantity. He experimented by inserting all sorts of strange materials—glass, bits of metal (including silver and gold), particles of shells—between the mantle and the shell of his pearl oysters. Mikimoto found that the most attractive blister pearls were those which had pieces of mother-of-pearl as their nucleus. So he concentrated upon that substance as a core for the blister pearls he produced and marketed throughout the world.

Meanwhile Mikimoto's experimentation continued. He groped about in the field of

A boat chugs steadily out of the bay, trailing its cargo of "working" pearl oysters. When winter approaches, the molluscs are taken to warmer waters, where they remain until spring.

oyster culture, trying to find the answer to the riddle of round pearls. He inserted pieces of mother-of-pearl in various parts of the bodies of hundreds of living oysters, and returned the molluscs to their underwater bamboo baskets, hoping that in time he would hit upon the key to producing a round pearl. As the years passed and he met with failure after failure, he became discouraged and despondent.

In 1893, only six months before the success of his blister pearl experiments, Mikimoto had been beset with a natural disaster: the dread "red tide," caused by the presence in the bay of poisonous plankton in huge numbers, nearly destroyed his crop of oysters. In 1905, another malignant red tide swept in to poison and suffocate over 800,000 of Mikimoto's oysters (only 150,000 oysters escaped the tide). The waters, turned blood red by the tide, washed the dying, stained oysters up on the shore. By now almost accustomed to heart-breaking frustration, Mikimoto sighed and undertook the dreary task of examining all the dead oysters. He wanted to salvage what he could of his blister pearl harvest, and perhaps he would find some remains of his insertion experiments.

In the demonstration room at Pearl Island, visitors can see the whole cycle of the pearl industry in a few short minutes, from insertion of the nucleus to harvesting.

Wearily he sat bent over basket after basket of rotting oysters, slitting the adductor muscle which holds the mollusc's shells together. Examining the shells to see if a pearl had been formed, he cut away those blister pearls which could be salvaged and discarded the rest of the oyster. Day after day he found nothing that would bring him closer to the solution of the puzzle of the round pearl. His experiments seemed to have been worthless. His money was almost gone. Only his wife had faith in him, and insisted that he go on. Almost at the point of total desperation, Mikimoto was ready to give up his apparently foolish dream after some 25 years of incredible hardship and research.

These freshly cleaned oysters are stacked in new cages, ready to be returned to the refreshing bay waters.

One of the first steps in processing pearls after the harvest is to sort them according to size. Here, a technician sifts the newly harvested pearls in a specially designed sieve.

THE PUZZLE IS SOLVED

Reaching for another basket of his experimental oysters, he slit open the topmost oyster. There was no pearl between the mantle and the gleaming inner shell of the oyster, although a nucleus had been planted inside somewhere. Then Mikimoto noticed an old scar on the adductor muscle. Inserting his knife into the old scar with little hope, he felt a faint hard substance resisting his knife. His hands began to tremble. In an instant his suspicion was confirmed: a perfectly round, lustrous pearl emerged from the innards of the slimy body of the dead oyster. Quickly reaching for another oyster from the same basket, he performed the same operation and found, much to his astonishment, another shining pearl in exactly the same place. His spirits soared.

Three more times he pried open oysters from that basket and each time he was rewarded by the glorious sight of a perfect, gleaming, round white pearl. All these oysters had had the nucleus inserted in the same place. Mikimoto knew he had found the secret and solved the mystery at last: Round pearls could be produced if the nucleus were inserted within the body of the oyster together with a piece of nacre-secreting mantle tissue.

In the meantime, however, others had also discovered the secret.

Tatsuhei Mise

In 1904, a humble Japanese carpenter, Tatsuhei Mise, had shown to a leader among Japanese marine scientists, Dr. Kishinoye, a round cultured pearl which he had developed. The pearl had been developed in an oyster with a lead nucleus covered with a piece of epithelium tissue from the mantle of another oyster.

The Japanese government, however, refused to grant Mise a patent for his method. But he did receive the first patent (in 1907) related to cultured pearl production, for a special kind of needle. Mise stated in his application for a patent that his needle was used to insert the nucleus "together with pieces of epithelium from the mantle . . . into the connective tissue and leave it inside the body of the oyster." So it is clear that Mise had a perfect understanding of the three basic requirements for the production of round cultured pearls.

The round nucleus is like a model about which the oyster deposits layers of nacre. Well inside the body of the oyster the pearl can thus develop freely, instead of becoming attached to the shell during the nacre-secreting process. The piece of nacre-secreting tissue from another oyster assures the formation of a pearl sac about the nucleus so that nacre will be deposited.

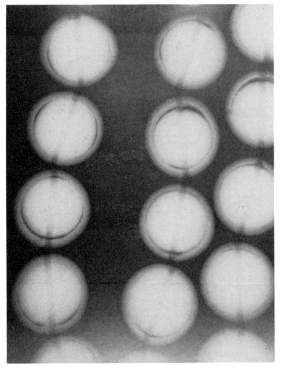

The only sure way to distinguish cultured pearls from natural pearls is to look "inside" the gems through X-rays. If there is an artificial nucleus, it will become immediately apparent. Here a technician readies the machine for an examination of a pearl necklace.

The pig-toe clam shell nuclei surrounded by nacre show us that this is a necklace of cultured pearls. The thicker the coating of nacre, the more valuable the pearls are. Running through the middle of each pearl can be seen the faint line of the silk thread with which the necklace is strung.

33

As with the natural pearl, the entrance of a foreign particle alone does not produce a pearl. In nature, as the foreign particle enters the oyster's body, it must carry some of the oyster's nacre-secreting cells along with it (some cells must be jarred loose as the foreign particle passes through or over the mantle) or no pearl will be formed.

It is the combination of these three factors (nucleus and epithelium inserted within the oyster's body) that enables an oyster to produce a lustrous pearl. Even so, a particularly stubborn oyster occasionally refuses to "co-operate," and a mis-shapen pearl—or no pearl at all—results.

Tokichi Nishikawa

Tokichi Nishikawa, another researcher working at about the same time as Mikimoto, applied for a patent on his method of producing a round pearl on October 23, 1907—five months after Mise. A scientist, Nishikawa later married Mikimoto's eldest daughter, Miyeko, but, perhaps because of his work, he and his father-in-law were not on good terms. When Nishikawa died at the early age of 35, the rights to his pearl cultivation methods were inherited by his son and his two assistants, the Fujita brothers. They eventually reconciled their differences with Mikimoto, and today the Nishikawa method for the nucleus insertion has been adopted by almost all pearl cultivators.

Nishikawa's method was essentially the same as that developed by Mise.

When Kokichi Mikimoto died, his grandson, Yoshitaka Mikimoto, became the manager of the huge family enterprises. Known as the "Pearl Prince," he was trained from boyhood by his grandfather.

The 14-karat gold Mikimoto Pearl Crown, set with nearly 1,600 pearls, was donated in 1957 to the National Cherry Blossom Festival in Washington, D.C. Each year it crowns the cherry blossom queen.

The Pearl King

Although Kokichi Mikimoto may not have been the first to produce the round cultured pearl, and did not originate the method he used so successfully to produce them, he is nevertheless the father of the industry because of his contributions and his great business acumen. Mikimoto's remarkable devotion to the development of the cultured pearl was the driving force behind the industry. Without his leadership, it is unlikely that the industry would exist today. Mikimoto felt he owed his success to the devotion of his wife, who encouraged him and cheerfully bore the years of poverty and sacrifice before Mikimoto succeeded. His one great sadness was that she did not live to see the development of the round cultured pearl.

Nominated as "The Pearl King" by a newspaper reporter in the 1920's, Mikimoto was thereafter known round the world by this affectionate name. His employees, however, never used this title in his presence, and instead called him Mikimoto *Taisho* (general). This was their way of showing admiration and respect.

So it has come about that what began in 1893 with one man in partnership with many shellfish is today an industry that employs many thousands of people and brings pleasure for very little money to many women and girls. In the pages that follow, we will see exactly how the basic cultured pearl process has been expanded into a giant industry.

In case bad weather or a sudden cold spell should menace the dangling oysters, the pearl farmers keep motor boats on the alert 24 hours a day. Within minutes, the huge rafts can be moved out of the danger zone.

THE SEA OF PEARLS

Cultured pearls are farmed today to some extent in the South Seas and Australia, but the bulk of the industry is located in Japan, which is ideally situated and possesses to the greatest degree the two essential ingredients of pearl farming: availability of pearl oysters and suitable climate. Ago Bay, on the south-eastern coast of Japan, and Toba Bay nearby, form the hub of the industry, and it is here that most of the huge Mikimoto pearl farms are located. Surrounded by luxuriant green hills, the sparkling deep blue waters of these bays provide a warm, snug home for the "working" pearl oyster. Ago Bay is honeycombed with lovely coves and inlets, and Toba Bay with islands and peninsulas, where the warm "black current" from the Philippines can sweep in, keeping the temperature of the water moderate (close to 20° C. or 68° F.) most of the year.

36

THE OYSTER BEDS

The pearl industry uses hundreds of thousands of oysters each year. Due to the foresight of the industry's pioneers, this number of pearl-building oysters is available today, either through collection of oyster eggs or cultivation, and the population is ever increasing.

The bulk of the oysters are obtained by "spat" collection. Each June, July and August when the oysters begin to spawn, preparations are made to "catch" some of the fertilized eggs which float through the waters near the giant motherbeds. A single mother oyster

Although they look fragile, the bamboo rafts are so sturdy that workers can walk on top of them without danger. However, like tightrope walkers, they must have an excellent sense of balance.

37

Scientists at the Japan National Pearl Research Laboratory keep a careful check on pearl harvesting conditions such as availability of food for the oysters, salinity of water, and the presence of minerals.

releases millions of tiny eggs. It is believed that as they float to the surface of the water, these eggs come in contact with spermatic fluid released by the male oysters in the beds. This process makes the waters look foamy and white nearly all summer long. But unless the tiny, free-floating eggs have a place to cling to, they are unable to develop into "spat" or baby oysters. The fertilized eggs shy away from brightly lighted places and smooth surfaces.

In order to capture as many of these future oysters as possible, rough-surfaced materials are suspended in the water to give the fertilized eggs a place to cling to and develop. Mikimoto patented a wire cage-like device, which is dipped first in hot tar and then in crushed sand. This is suspended from buoyed wooden or bamboo rafts above the oyster beds. Tarred and sanded ropes are sometimes hung instead of cages. More frequently today *cryptomeria* (Japanese cedar) branches are hung from the rafts, as they have been found most protective for the eggs.

In about 25 days the eggs develop into spat. In October, when the spat are at least a month old, the oyster-festooned branches or cages are raised. Each individual cultivator is entitled to keep the spat which develop from his own oysters, and most cultivators do take the necessary steps to catch the eggs released during the spawning season. Those baby oysters which have not been caught by private farmers, but come from the so-called motherbeds, are auctioned off to pearl farmers by the Mie Prefecture Fisheries Union, a co-operative, non-profit organization to which most of the pearl cultivators belong. (Mie Prefect is the province of Honshu Island that includes Ago Bay.) The union supervises this essential part of the industry, and ensures that the huge oyster beds which constitute one of Japan's most valuable natural resources are cared for and protected. If the union did not protect the beds, selfish and greedy private interests might deplete them, just as natural oyster beds were depleted and destroyed in the 18th and 19th centuries.

Spat collection is of the utmost importance to many small cultivators, for they can build up beds with a small investment, much less than if they had to buy their eggs. Huge cultivators like the Mikimoto company are able to collect a large portion of the spat they need in this way, too; not only is this of financial benefit but it results in less drain on the resources of the motherbeds administered by the Fisheries Union.

The "ama" use wooden tubs in which to deposit their catches of seafood and mother oysters. The tubs are also used as floats.

Scientists do not all agree about the reproductive habits of an oyster. It is believed that oysters experience a sex reversal (the spontaneous change of a male oyster into a female or vice versa). Occasionally oysters have been found to have changed sex several times during their life-span, usually at the height of the spawning season. Thus no special precautions are taken to sort or separate male and female oysters. Instead, the rough-surfaced "catchers" are simply suspended over the oyster beds and cages, and the cultivators hope for the best. It is unlikely that in a large collection of oysters the males would overbalance the females, and therefore some eggs are always fertilized and collected.

Under the supervision of the union, also, some larger pearl oysters are taken from the huge motherbeds off the coast of southern Honshu in and near Ago Bay, and made available at auction to pearl cultivators. The oysters are carefully lifted from their beds by skilled women divers, and are subsequently sold at auction.

These two sources supply nearly 85 per cent of the pearl oysters needed each year in Japan. Additional oysters may sometimes be brought in from other parts of Japan and sold through the Fisheries Union.

When the "ama" rise to the surface, their haunting "sea whistle" fills the air. The musical sound is produced because the "ama" breathe only through their mouths to increase lung power.

40

During their rest periods, the "ama" cook light snacks on the beach and play with their children. Most pearl farms treat their employees extremely well, and encourage a "family" feeling. Within a few years these little children may begin their diving training.

THE DIVERS

Centuries before cultured pearl farming began, the graceful women divers called "ama" traditionally dived for natural pearls, and to collect edible seaweed and shellfish to feed their families. The ama were generally fishermen's wives, and they worked to supplement the family income. Since women are naturally endowed with a thicker protective layer of fat, men almost never work as divers in Japanese waters.

Most ama begin their training between the ages of 5 and 10, and continue diving even into their 60's or 70's, with only a brief interruption for childbearing. Traditionally, the profession is passed on from mother to daughter. Wearing the centuries-old white costume (they believe that sharks, eels, and other marine enemies are repelled by white), the ama are enchanting to watch as they work. Like mermaids in white, they seem to be dancing in slow motion under the water. Their simple, long-sleeved high-necked shirts and wrap-around skirts tied between the legs protect them from the cold; except in mid-summer, the air is even colder than the water.

In the early days of pearl farming, the ama dived down to the natural oyster beds to

Many different kinds of boats are used by the "ama." This is one of the home-made boats operated by a small group of free-lance "ama," and it is used for fishing during the "off" season.

inspect, collect, and, if necessary, move the pearl-building oysters. In those times pearls, oysters and ama were inseparable, but modernized equipment and techniques have dissolved this romantic partnership. Nowadays, the pearl oysters are organized neatly in cages or suspended from cords on rafts. It is a simple matter to clean, protect, observe and move the molluscs about without the help of the ama. Even so, the ama still make important contributions to the pearl industry.

They utilize their ancient skills diving in the spring to gather oysters from the huge motherbeds. Removing oysters by machinery would greatly damage and disturb the carefully-tended motherbeds, so the skilled ama must remove them gently by hand.

The ama are often needed, too, after a disaster has struck a pearl farm. During a typhoon, for example, many rafts are shattered, and wire baskets or cages torn from the rafts and tossed wildly about the bay area, where they sink finally to the ocean floor in disarray. The unfortunate pearl farmer must hire ama to salvage what remains of his crop and equipment after the storm has abated.

There are two kinds of ama: those who work "alone" (kachido) and boat divers (funado). The kachido are each equipped with a wooden tub, which is attached to the waist by a long cord. In addition, each diver covers her face with a rubber and plastic diving mask, and carries a sturdy knife with which to pry loose the oysters or seaweed she must collect.

42

Visitors to the observation platform at Mikimoto's Pearl Island in Ago Bay enjoy watching the "ama" demonstrate diving techniques.

This close-up view of the rafts shows how they are buoyed up in the water by tarred barrels. The most modern rafts are buoyed up by polyethylene cylinders.

43

Mikimoto's $1,000,000 (£350,000) model of the American Liberty Bell is fashioned of pure silver, diamonds and 12,250 brilliant pearls.

Although the *kachido* divers operate in groups from one large boat, in the water each woman is responsible for her own safety. The boats do no more than transport the *kachido* divers and their catches to and from the motherbeds. When a diver needs to catch her breath, she surfaces, deposits her catch in her buoyant wooden tub, and holds on to the tub until she is able to go down again.

The ama dive for approximately two hours, staying under the water for one or two minutes at a time, and then rest for perhaps half an hour on the shore. On the sheltered beach, they wrap themselves in warm robes, change their wet costumes, and huddle next to a crackling fire to keep warm. They eat a light snack of roasted shellfish during each rest period to prevent overeating at any one time of the 6- to 8-hour working day.

The *funado* or boat diver has more help, and is thus able to dive in deeper waters for longer periods of time without tiring. A boat diver generally works with her husband as a

44

team, so she does not need a tub to serve as a float. Instead a *funado* fastens a net to her waist to receive her catch, together with a weighted life-line.

Her husband is usually kept very busy running the boat and helping her. She dives with the aid of a pulley system: her weighted life-line is thrown into the sea, and she follows it down to the sandy ocean floor, where the strange undersea world is almost as familiar to her as our town or city is to us. When her breath gives out, her net is likely to be full of craggy-shelled oysters. She tugs her life-line to signal her husband that it is time to surface. He slowly turns the pulley crank to which her life-line is fastened, hauling her gently but steadily to the surface. In this way the diver's strength is not taxed.

When an ama surfaces, an eerie whistling sound is heard. Believing that it increases lung power, the ama breathe only through their mouths, and their haunting "sea whistle" fills the air with a music which seems to come from the sea itself.

Work for the ama is seasonal at best. The diving season, beginning in April, provides only about 100 days of work before it ends in September. Thus many divers must supplement their incomes during the rest of the year by working at the pearl farms, inserting nuclei into oysters, demonstrating diving techniques for visitors to the pearl farms, or diving for shellfish in the Pacific Ocean. While diving is one of the most picturesque and romantic aspects of the cultured pearl industry, the ama's work is gruelling physical toil, requiring persistence and patience.

Sometimes the rafts are loaded right on the boats to be moved to warmer waters, especially if the trip is long and weather reports foreboding.

Neatly stacked in their baskets, the oysters are suspended from rafts in the warm waters of the bay.

THE OYSTER'S FIRST YEARS

After baby oysters have been obtained by the pearl farmer, they are sorted, examined, and placed according to age in sturdy wire or nylon containers. Suspended from wooden rafts by means of strong ropes, the containers are set out in sheltered water. As the oysters increase in size, they are gradually transferred to larger and larger containers until they are three years old—old enough to begin their life work.

WHERE THE OYSTER LIVES

Though Japan is completely surrounded by the sea, the areas suitable for pearl culture are actually rather limited. Pearl oysters thrive best in places where a river can empty some fresh water into the area during the rainy season. The current of fresh water carries the oyster's food to it, and this is essential, for, as we know, the oyster cannot find its own food. Too much fresh water can endanger the oyster's life, however, so the balance between fresh and salt water must be exactly right.

Not only must the current and fresh water content of the bay be suitable, but so must the temperature of the water. The pearl oyster cannot adjust itself to sudden changes in temperature, either hot or cold. Even if a sudden temperature change did not kill an oyster, the lustre and quality of its pearl would certainly suffer.

Nestled in the quiet waters of warm sheltered bays, the oyster thrives. However, the pearl cultivators take no chances, and to ensure the continuing health of their oysters throughout the relatively cold winters, the pampered oysters from Ago and Toba Bays, suspended in

A special thermometer is used to check the temperature of the water periodically. Pearl oysters cannot withstand extreme temperature changes.

Every 3 months or so, barges like this carry workers out to the rafts to clean the oysters.

their baskets from rafts, are towed southwest each winter to the waters of Kyushu Island, where thermal springs under the water add to the warmth. Farms like those at Ago Bay bustle with activity when the oysters return home in the spring.

In land agriculture, the soil becomes exhausted when the same crops are cultivated in the same spots year after year. A similar weakening or exhaustion occurs in the bays where pearl oysters are cultivated if the molluscs are kept in the same area for several years. Therefore, the waters are given an occasional rest from pearl farming. Changing the site of a pearl farm every few years helps to ensure prime health in the oysters being bred, and gives a weary site a chance to lie fallow so it can renew itself.

So the adolescent oysters journey about a great deal while growing up, even though by themselves they are practically unable to travel at all.

A PEARL IS BORN

When the oyster is at least two and preferably three years old, it is mature enough to begin its life's-work: building a lustrous pearl or two. (The circles—annular rings—on the oyster's shell show how old it is.) During its babyhood and adolescence the oyster has been kept clean and warm, and provided with shelter and nourishment. In return, the oyster in a sense repays this kindness by producing a shimmering pearl at its caretaker's request. As we know, the deliberate insertion of a nucleus, instead of the accidental entrance of a foreign particle, is the major difference between a cultured and a natural pearl.

Mikimoto discovered that the oyster would cover almost any foreign substance with nacre. However, nacre is relatively soft and easily drilled. He finally determined that an equally soft and chemically similar nucleus was the best for producing a satisfactory cultured pearl. In addition, drilling a hole for stringing a necklace heats the pearl and causes the

48

nacre to expand. Therefore, it is essential that the nucleus expand at the same rate or the pearl will shatter.

After years of experimentation, the ideal nucleus substance was found: the so-called "pig-toe" clam shell from America—from the Tennessee River, a branch of the Ohio and Mississippi Rivers. (The name "pig-toe" comes from the shell's resemblance to a pig's toe.) Except for a shell that was formerly available from the Yangtze River in China, no other substance has proved as satisfactory as this, and in recent years the demand has been so heavy that a serious shortage has occurred. The Tennessee Valley Authority has been conducting intensive research to solve this critical problem.

In the meantime, almost 6 tons of the pig-toe clam shells are being shipped from the United States to Japan every year. The meat is removed before shipment, and the shells cleaned. In Japan at special factories, the clam shell is cut first in large chunks, then smaller

Pig-toe clam shells, from which the nuclei for pearls are made, come from the Tennessee River, which flows into the Ohio and Mississippi Rivers. To gather the shells, a "brail," carrying hundreds of smooth hooks without barbs, is lowered into the water and dragged slowly across the bottom. The molluscs close their shells on the hooks, and are collected when the brail is lifted from the water.

The clams are steamed so their shells will open, to facilitate removal of the meat. The scrubbed shells are then shipped to Japan.

In special factories in Japan, the pig-toe shells are prepared for grinding. First they are broken into large strips.

The interior shell is chipped from the rough outer shell, and then hammered into fairly small squares.

chunks, and finally ground into spheres. The balls are sized to range from 2.5 millimetres to 8 millimetres, and are polished until they are perfectly smooth. The glowing white nuclei are then sold to the cultivators, who purchase them according to the size of pearls they want to produce. The larger the nucleus, the larger the pearl will be, but also the more difficult for the oyster to retain. With a supply of pig-toe nuclei, and a healthy stock of oysters, the cultivator is ready to start production.

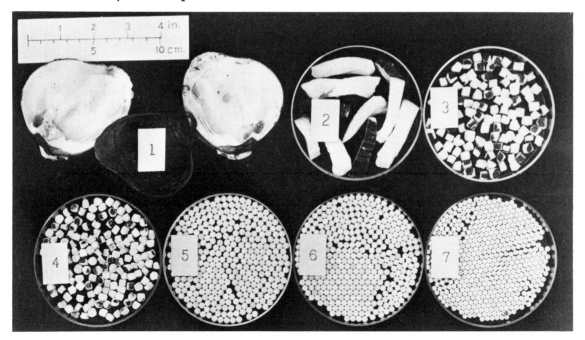

The pig-toe squares are polished in four stages until they become smooth spheres. Prepared in various sizes, the gleaming white nuclei are then ready for the pearl farmers.

51

This is a microscopic view of a cross-section of a cultured pearl, showing the point at which the layers of nacre deposited by the oyster meet the pig-toe shell nucleus. The crystals of the pig-toe shell are formed in a smooth horizontal plane, while the deposits of nacre rise vertically.

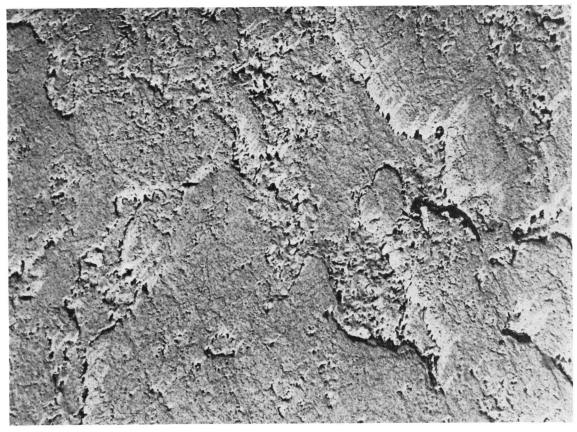

The surface of a cultured pearl magnified 14,000 times by an electron microscope shows the slight variations in texture which produce the beautiful lustre of the pearl.

Another picture of the crystalline surface of a cultured pearl magnified 6,000 times.

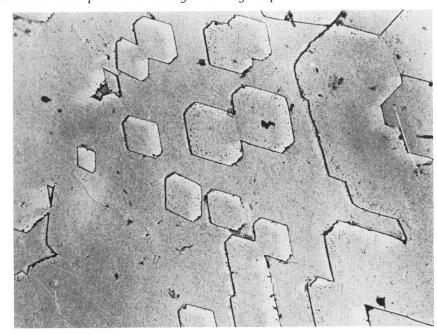

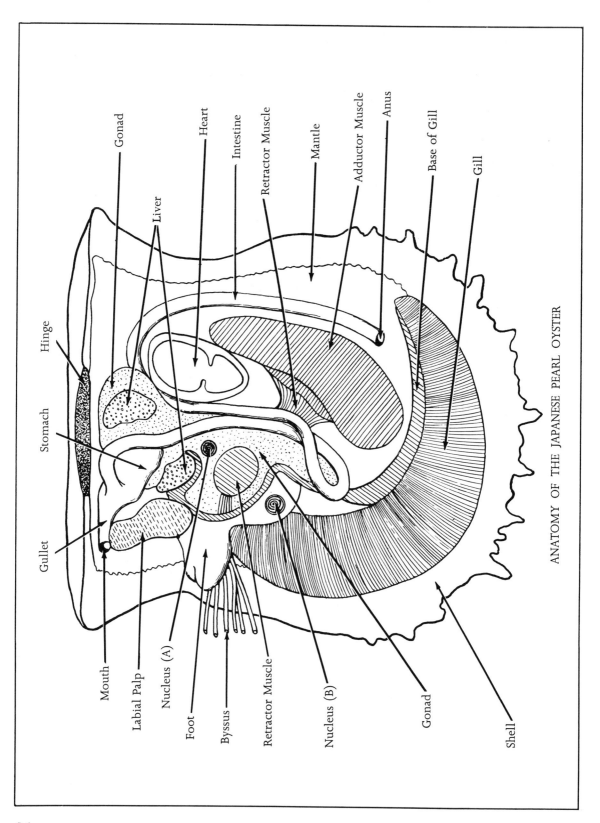

ANATOMY OF THE JAPANESE PEARL OYSTER

Gonad

Liver

Heart

Intestine

Retractor Muscle

Mantle

Adductor Muscle

Anus

Base of Gill

Gill

Hinge

Stomach

Gullet

Mouth

Labial Palp

Nucleus (A)

Foot

Byssus

Retractor Muscle

Nucleus (B)

Gonad

Shell

54

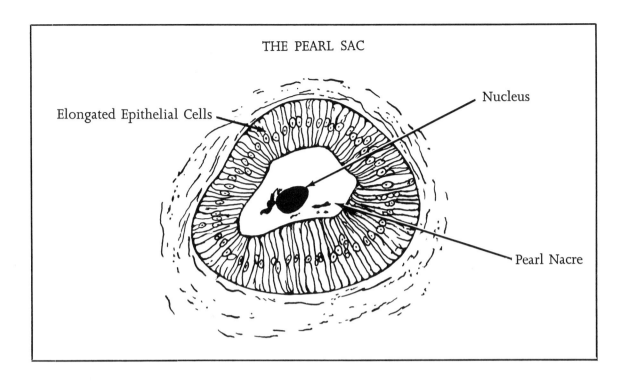

THE PEARL SAC

Elongated Epithelial Cells

Nucleus

Pearl Nacre

INSERTION OF THE NUCLEUS

Twenty-four hours before nucleus insertion is to take place, the oysters are towed towards the pearl farm. They spend the night in their cages, which are tied to the farm's dock. Early the next morning, workers lift basket after basket of oysters from the water on to the dock. The oysters are removed and placed in dry containers in a shady spot.

Before long, a few oysters cautiously begin to open their shells. Within half an hour, almost all the oysters have opened their shells. (Those which have not are returned to their baskets and submerged for another 24 hours.) As soon as the shells open, a worker slips a wooden wedge in the crack so that the oyster will not be able to close again. When all the oysters are pegged, they are transferred to a sunny room where experts will implant the nuclei. These men and women have been trained for years to perform this precise, delicate operation.

Seated at wide tables, each operator awaiting the oysters has, on a block of wood, long strips of already prepared living epithelial tissues from other pearl oysters, to be inserted along with the nuclei. One oyster must die to furnish the tissue to accompany every 14 or 15 inserted nuclei. The epithelium is cut from the mantle (see photograph), and the rough edges trimmed away. Then each strip of epithelium is cut cross-wise, to make 15 or more tiny squares. The tissue will remain alive up to 2 hours, and must be used before it dies.

The operator secures a pegged oyster in a clamping device directly in front of her, and either leaves the wooden wedge or replaces it with a retractor, which can be adjusted to force the shells further apart. Her tools resemble those of a dentist. Swiftly, through the narrow opening, she makes a small incision (about $\frac{1}{2}$ inch long) into the body of the oyster at "A" (the gonad or ovary) or "B" (the connective tissue) as shown in the diagram. Immediately

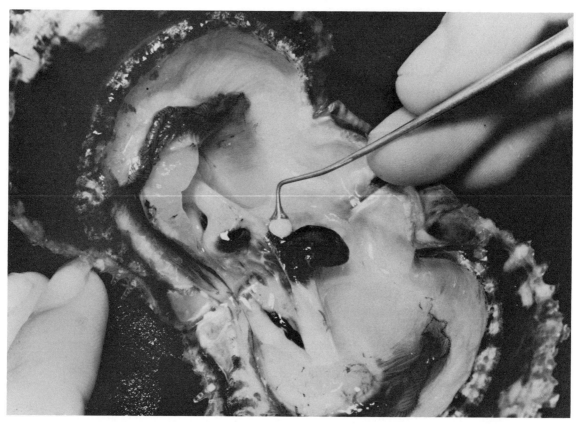

The nucleus, which adheres to the wet cupped tool by suction, is embedded into the gonad of the oyster. This not only makes it difficult for the oyster to eject the foreign object, but allows nacre from the grafted tissue to be deposited all round the nucleus. However, if the oyster's shells are opened as wide as shown here, it dies, so the nucleus insertion must be performed through a very narrow opening.

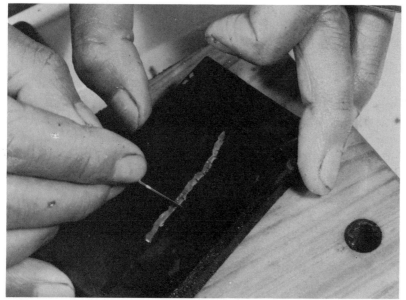

Special tools are used to cut the epithelium tissue before insertion.

That part of the mantle which secretes nacre is cut from a live oyster. With the rough edges trimmed away, the tissue is cut into 15 to 20 tiny squares. Each square will be inserted together with a nucleus in another oyster. (Sometimes two squares and two nuclei are used.) The "foreign" tissue will form a "pearl sac" about the nucleus until a pearl has been formed.

The oyster is secured in a clamp directly in front of the operator. Nearby are nuclei in various sizes, pure water, tools similar to those of a dentist, and squares of prepared epithelium tissue grafts.

thereafter, she skilfully slips the prepared epithelium square into place within the body of the oyster, followed by the round nucleus which she has first dipped in water. She takes special care to make sure that the nucleus stays directly next to the bit of epithelium graft, for if it does not, no pearl sac will be formed. This procedure may be reversed or the operator may slip in the nucleus with the epithelium adhering to it, but the two foreign objects must always lie next to each other.

As soon as the nucleus and graft are in place, the retractor or wedge is removed, and the oyster is instantly placed in a container of sea water. The operation has lasted less than 60 seconds, but it will affect the oyster's whole life. In a little while the oyster is returned to its cage and suspended once more in the sea water, where it will spend the next six weeks recuperating from the shock of the operation.

58

Three-year-old oysters are brought to this room in trays for nucleus insertion. The skilled operators were trained for 2 years to perform this precise, delicate operation.

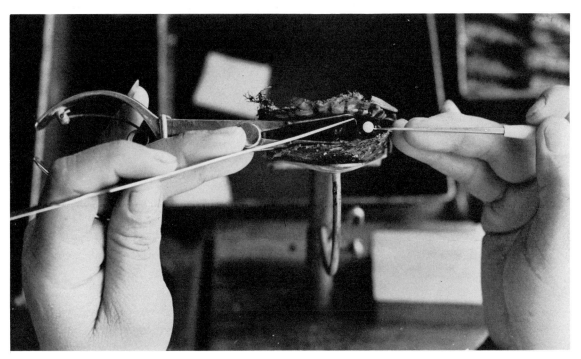

Here, note how tiny the epithelium graft tissue (dangling from the edge of the long tool on the left) is in comparison with the nucleus. The retractor (left) is adjustable, so the operator can vary the size of the opening according to the size of the nucleus to be inserted.

59

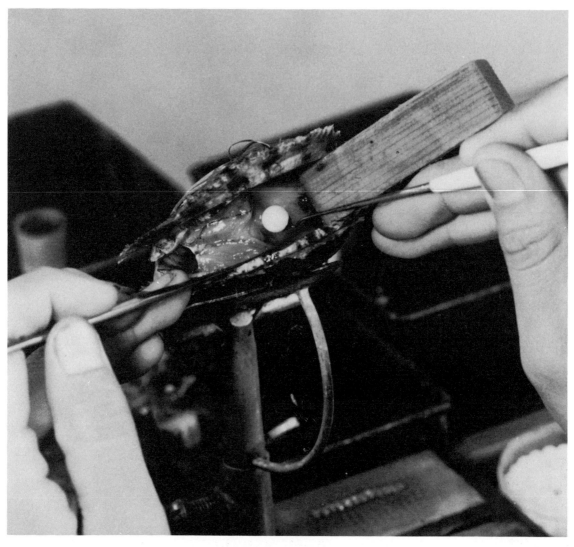

This close-up view of the insertion process shows just how small the opening must be in order to preserve the oyster's life. The operator must insert the nucleus and graft tissue swiftly (in approximately 30 seconds), and remove the wooden peg or retractor. The oyster is immediately submerged in a container of salt water to begin its long convalescence.

Seven to ten days after the operation, the foreign epithelium should begin to form a pearl sac round the nucleus, and begin to deposit layers of nacre about the nucleus.

When the recovery period is over, the oysters are raised once again. The fragile, tender shell of each mollusc is carefully inspected and gently scraped to remove any accumulated barnacles and slimy moss. Oysters who have not survived are removed and discarded. As many as 50 per cent of the oysters die after the operation. The healthy oysters are then suspended from the rafts in sparkling clean cages, and towed back out to pre-arranged positions in the bay.

THE OYSTER'S HOME

During the next 2 to 4 years the oysters are kept housed in one of two preferred ways: hanging in "free suspension," or stacked in wire or nylon baskets. The rectangular wire baskets are hand-made, and are about 18 inches long by about 12 inches wide. Before they can be used they are dipped in hot tar, which serves as a disinfectant, and then cooled in the open air. Each full-sized basket can accommodate 48 to 50 neatly separated oysters, but nowadays only 15 to 24 oysters are placed in each basket in order to ensure a plentiful food supply for each oyster. After the molluscs have been placed in position inside the cages, the lids are fastened down securely with rope. The baskets are then suspended from large rafts at certain depths. (The nylon baskets, although smaller, are preferred because they do not rust.)

The wooden rafts consist of either cedar logs or bamboo poles lashed together to form large frames. Walking on a raft can be quite a trick. Sometimes the rafts are lashed in such a way that portions may be separated to facilitate towing when the oysters must be moved. On each raft, a tile plate is affixed, giving the name of the operator (owner), the age of the oysters, the size of the nucleus, the date of the submersion, and sometimes the depth to which the cages are lowered. It is from these tiles that the cleaners and later the harvesters get their information.

Huge tarred barrels are fastened to the undersides of the cedar rafts to buoy them up out of the water. The newest type of raft consists of rope (instead of wood) and polyethylene air-filled balloons (instead of barrels) as buoys. Wooden rafts have a tendency to splinter in a storm, and are heavier than the rope rafts.

Most modern pearl farmers find that nylon baskets with wire frames are far superior to the heavy, cumbersome wire baskets.

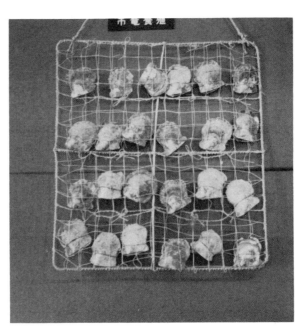

Thousands of oysters nowadays can be transferred from one place to another in a matter of hours. Each sturdy basket contains from 15 to 24 molluscs. In the early days of pearl farming, the oysters were placed in groups at the bottom of the bay. Not only did this leave the oysters without protection from dangerous marine enemies and climate, but gathering them was a Herculean task requiring weeks of diving.

The baskets are hung from the rafts, spaced so that the cages will not bump into each other. The sturdy ropes used to tie the baskets to the rafts are very long, but their whole length is not normally used. Extra length is saved to enable the pearl cultivator to lower the baskets should a sudden cold spell or red tide menace his oysters.

The free suspension method is quite different. A minuscule hole is drilled through the shell of the oyster and a nylon thread is passed through it. Some cultivators thread several oysters on one long thread and wind the thread on a tarred rope. Others thread only one oyster on a short length of nylon thread and tie each one individually to the tarred rope. In both methods, the oyster-laden ropes are suspended from enormous bamboo pole floats. Since bamboo is extremely buoyant, these rafts float right on top of the water without

In the "free suspension" method, a minuscule hole is drilled through the oyster's shell. A thread is attached, and the molluscs are fastened to tarred ropes which are suspended from rafts. Although they are completely exposed to marine enemies when they hang in "free suspension," the oysters are also more exposed to food, so they grow faster than do caged oysters.

additional support. Thus they can be moved about more easily than the rafts with cumbersome wire baskets.

Another advantage of the free suspension method is that the oysters are able to feed with ease. The plankton in the water flows about the oysters without obstruction, and the oysters —and their pearls—increase in size much sooner than caged oysters do. However, the dangling oysters are perilously exposed to their sea enemies at the same time—a serious disadvantage.

Many new suspension methods are under experimentation, and perhaps in the near future nylon nets will replace the more cumbersome wire or wire and nylon cages. This would mean a great saving of time, money and effort for the pearl farmers. Transportation, cleaning, and tarring will all become simpler tasks if nylon nets are proved practical.

63

DANGERS OF THE DEEP

The pearl cultivator cannot relax just because his oysters are set out in the bay, for the molluscs are constantly in danger. Hazards lurk in every direction: the air, the sea, and even the ocean floor. Many men and women working practically round the clock are needed to protect the vulnerable oysters.

Marine Enemies

First of all, many creatures of the sea prey upon the oysters dangling from rafts or imprisoned in their cages. Sleek eels can slip through the wire barriers to suck the oysters from their craggy shells, especially when the oysters' shells are slightly open (while feeding). Sharks can break through the barriers and thrash about under a raft. The hideous black porgy and the comical globefish also feed on oysters, in particular very young molluscs. The octopus can encircle an oyster and hold its shells tightly closed until it is crushed or suffocated. Octopi have been known to consume more than a dozen pearl oysters a night in summer, though the wire cages have made this much more difficult in recent years.

Barnacles (little clinging animals that attach themselves to rocks and shells), sponges and

Coarse netting placed inside the baskets protects the oysters to some extent from eels and octopi, while allowing the tiny plankton upon which the oysters feed to pass through the openings easily.

64

Barnacles and seaweed fastened to the shells impede the oysters' feeding activity. Workers gently scrape the encrusted shells with a blunt-edged knife until the oysters are clean again. At the same time a few oysters are opened to check on the progress of the pearls.

seaweeds create havoc by festooning the cages, thereby obstructing the passage of incoming food. This does considerable damage, interfering with the growth of the oyster. Periodic cleaning of the cages and shells eliminates this source of peril to some extent.

Dangers in the Elements

Although normally protected from sudden temperature changes by the warm currents, the waters of pearl culture bays are occasionally endangered by cold currents and sudden, extreme air temperature changes. The only possible defence is to tow the oysters quickly to warmer waters.

Typhoon warnings nowadays come from weather stations scattered round the coasts of Japan. If there is time, the oysters are quickly removed from the imperilled area, but if a typhoon strikes directly across the bay, terrible losses are suffered as cages and rafts are demolished and scattered on the ocean floor.

Earthquakes are not rare in Japan, though most are slight. The ocean floor is set violently into motion, old openings close, and new fissures burst open. Often the oyster beds on the ocean floor are swallowed in the process. Huge clouds of mud swirl round the hanging cages, suffocating the oysters even if they have not been torn loose from their anchoring rafts.

65

The Red Tide

The most dread disaster of all is the catastrophic red tide. Although red tide has been known since the 16th century, not until 1858 did an investigation of it in the coastal waters round Bombay show the basic cause to be plankton organisms. In 1899, Tokichi Nishikawa investigated a red tide near Ago Bay and was able to isolate the organism which caused the damage, but he was unable to shed light on the reason for the tide.

The frightful red tide (normal plankton can vary from pale lemon yellow to bright green) is fatal to fish, molluscs, crustaceans, and any other form of aquatic animal life which breathes by gills or in which respiration is controlled by pores or small body openings, such as sponges. Although the actual method by which the great invasion of plankton causes death is not entirely clear, death may be caused by any one or more of the following:

1. The tiny organisms multiply to such huge numbers that they consume nearly all the oxygen in the water, leaving none for the molluscs. Therefore, the oysters suffocate.

2. The water becomes so thick and clouded with the millions of plankton that the gills or other breathing apparatus of the sea creatures are clogged, also causing suffocation.

3. The living plankton may secrete poisonous substances which are fatal to the oysters.

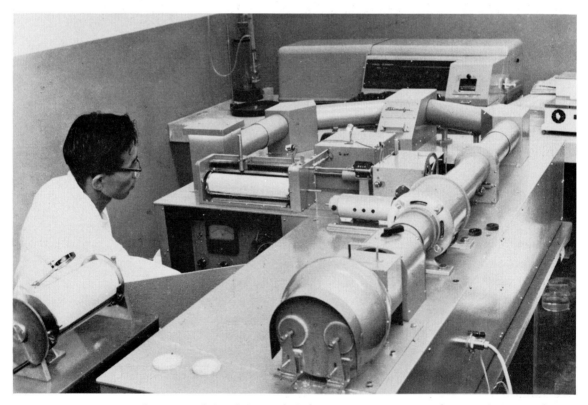

A Japanese scientist at the National Pearl Research Laboratory examines one of a sample batch of pearl oysters to determine how environment affects the oyster and the development of the pearl.

66

Some of the larger Japanese exporters present ropes of pearls fastened with beautiful silk tassels for sale to wholesale buyers from other nations.

4. When most of the plankton finally die, they still may continue to exude poisonous substances as they decompose. The oysters and other marine animals apparently cannot fight this poison.

Constant research is being carried out in an effort to find the way in which to combat the horrible red tide.

The Human Element

As we have seen, the establishment of a pearl farm requires great expense and years of patient, exhausting effort. Some people want to start "the easy way," and so pearl farmers are continually menaced by "pearl pirates." These unscrupulous men slip into a bay in the dark of night and make away with baskets or even whole rafts of nucleus-filled oysters,

Usually a number of strands of closely matched pearls are gathered together into hanks. This practice makes it easier for the buyers to make them into necklaces.

despite the precautions of 24-hour guards and searchlights playing over the oyster beds all night long.

Although the rafts of each pearl farmer are labelled or branded, it is a simple matter to remove cages from rafts. This makes it impossible to identify the stolen oysters, whose craggy shells do not lend themselves to identifying marks. Many oysters are lost to pirates each year.

WORKERS ON THE PEARL FARMS

In addition to the graceful ama, many skilled workers staff the pearl farms. Men are needed to operate the motor boats which carry the divers to the oyster beds and which transport the oysters to warm waters when necessary. A house-boat (a raft covered with a sloping roof) must also carry workers to the rafts in the bay when it is time to clean the oysters' shells. Approximately ten women staff each cleaning boat. They stand round a rectangular plank table, and with a blunt, spatula-shaped knife scrape the encrusted shells, examining them at the same time to make sure the oysters are alive and healthy. (A diseased oyster, or a dead one, will have a partially opened shell.) A few oysters are opened to determine the progress of the pearls. Then sturdy men replace the cleaned oysters in freshly scrubbed cages, and return them to their marine home so they may continue working. The seaweed-covered cages are taken to shore to be cleaned for re-use.

Besides the technicians who insert the nuclei, pearl farms need many men and women to harvest the pearls, and specially trained workers to sort, grade, drill and assemble necklaces. The pearl industry now employs more than 10,000 people in Japan alone (not counting people who work in sales). The workers almost always share in the profits of the pearl industry, a practice which Mikimoto initiated when he founded his pioneering pearl farms.

Japanese pearl farmers have always encouraged a family feeling among their employees, and the relationship has proved beneficial for both sides. The employees are among the best-treated in the world, and it is not unusual for the company to provide nearly all their needs and wants. Mikimoto, the leader in this field, gave his employees such working benefits as Japan's first 6-day work week, free haircuts, medical care, and even marriage counselling, as well as high pay. In return, the workers are on the whole devoted, scrupulously honest, loyal, and extremely hard-working.

Half-drilled cultured pearls are mounted in place on gold jewelry in this workshop in Japan.

A more modern method of cleaning consists of holding the oysters next to a rough-surfaced revolving disc. This must be done with great care to avoid damaging the fragile shells.

HARVEST TIME

There is never a dull moment at the pearl farms. In the spring, activity is at a fever pitch as the workers are kept busy inserting the nuclei. The summer diving and egg-gathering season follows directly, and in-between moments are filled with constant cleaning and inspecting of the working pearl oysters and the babies. The winter season is the most exciting of all, however, for it is at this time that the long years of arduous toil are rewarded by the reaping of the harvest—the long-awaited pearls.

It takes an oyster three to four years to cover a nucleus sufficiently with nacre to form a sizeable pearl. If the pearl is left within the body of the oyster longer, the mollusc will continue to deposit layers of nacre about it, but often much of the lustre and sheen of the pearl is lost. Therefore most oysters are harvested between three and four years after the implantation of the nucleus.

Lustre is what gives the pearl its unique and fascinating quality; poor lustre renders a pearl commercially worthless. The pearl consists largely of a substance called calcium carbonate, together with a small amount (about 5 per cent) of protein. The reflection of light from this combination of substances produces the prism-like gleam we call lustre. Since the oyster's biological functions are slowed in cool water, less protein is produced, and the resulting refraction of light from the calcium carbonate crystals is greater. Thus lustre is at its greatest under cold water conditions. This is the reason the harvesting takes place during the cold months: December, January and February.

As winter approaches and it is time to move the oyster crop to warm waters, the oysters that have been cultivated for three to four years are left behind. As the boats chug merrily away from the bay with their cargo of working oysters trailing behind, the bay, dotted now only sparsely with rafts, may look quite forlorn. But there is much hustle and bustle as the workers prepare to harvest the remaining pearl oysters.

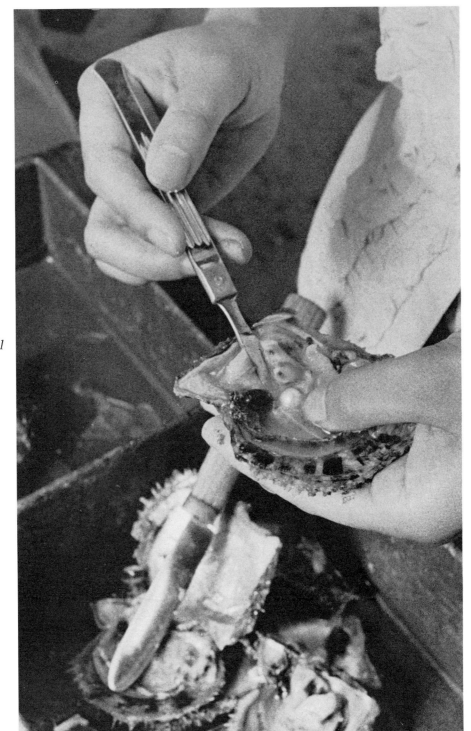

A shimmering pearl
emerges from the
slimy body of the
oyster.

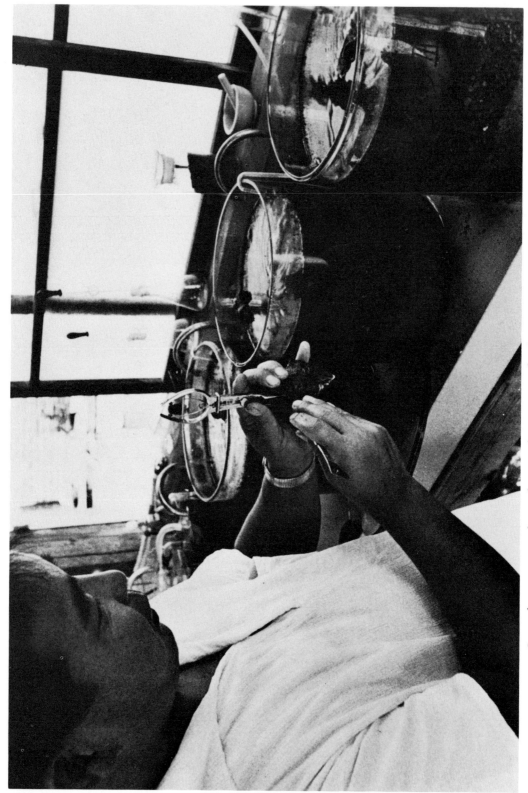

Research to improve the quality—and quantity—of cultured pearls is constantly being carried out. Despite the meticulous care now given to the oysters, over 50 per cent die after the nucleus-insertion operation.

After the pearls are sorted for quality and hue, they are divided according to size and shape. A special tool helps the sorter.

HARVESTING

Although methods vary slightly from farm to farm, basically the harvesting procedure is this: long slotted plank tables are set out on the open beach. A worker sits next to each slot, under which a container is placed to receive the harvested pearls. Workers bring the baskets of pearl oysters up on to the beach, and empty the molluscs into wooden containers on the tables.

Skilfully slitting through the oyster's adductor muscle with a specially designed knife, the operator opens the shell and scoops out the part of the oyster containing the pearl. He empties the contents (pearl and all) into a container under the slot. The only part of the oyster which remains in the shell is the adductor muscle (see diagram on page 54). This muscle is usually later fried in deep fat at an evening feast for the harvest workers. This is the only part of the pearl oyster which is eaten.

When the containers under the tables are full, other workers empty them into a vat

Using a paddle with 100 slots, this worker counts thousands of pearls each minute.

containing quicklime and sea water. The vat is agitated, to separate the pearls from the oyster meat and any sand or shell particles which may be present. The pearls are then removed and placed in another tub of sea water, which contains an amount of salt equal to the amount of pearls to be washed (that is, two pounds of salt to two pounds of pearls, for example). After being thoroughly washed in this mixture, the newly-born pearls are tenderly rinsed and dried with a soft cloth.

Harvesting of course ends the life of the pearl oyster, and this is the reason so much effort goes into the collection of spat and the protection of the motherbeds.

SORTING

The first task in readying the pearls for market is to "cull" (separate) the worthless from the valuable pearls. Nearly 40 per cent of the harvested pearls have no commercial value, and of the remaining 60 per cent, perhaps only 5 or 10 per cent will be flawless, round, white jewels.

Rough sorting is a job which requires great skill and good judgment, and the women who sort the so-called "bulk" harvest must be specially trained to sort by eye. Even though a pearl is malformed or strange in shape or hue, it may have many uses. Half pearls can be made into earrings or buttons. Baroque pearls may be serviceable as pendants or brooches. Not quite perfect pearls can be "stripped" (the topmost layers of nacre carefully removed) or cut so that part of the pearl can be salvaged. Almost all pearls have a slight spot, but this does not hamper its use on a necklace, as the hole can be drilled through the imperfection.

When the pearls have been sorted as to quality, they are counted. Since each harvest yields thousands of pearls, a special paddle with slots for 100 pearls is used to speed counting. Experienced counters can count 100 pearls each second with this paddle.

Working under a cold north light, these girls have been specially trained to sort pearls according to hue. It is impossible for the untrained eye to distinguish the many variations.

HUES AND WEIGHT

The gradations of tones in pearls are almost infinite, but most of these are indistinguishable to the eye of the average person. The most easily recognized tones are pure white, gold and black (actually black pearls are really dark blue or grey). The pearl industry recognizes the following six categories: white, cream, pink, green, gold and black, but the variations within these categories are almost limitless.

The women who sort pearls for tone do their work under a cold north light, separating the pearls quickly into a number of single-toned heaps. The onlooker is amazed to see the pearls once they are separated; suddenly many different gradations of tone are apparent, while in bulk the pearls seem to be quite similar in hue.

The next step is to weigh the pearls, for the heavier the pearl, the more valuable it is. Two pearls which look exactly alike may differ in weight, so this process must be carried out with great precision. As we explained earlier, the unit of weight for the pearl is the momme, or grain. Thus an 8-grain pearl is worth less than a 10-grain pearl if the quality of both is the same.

Once the pearls have been graded, counted, and sorted as to weight, tone, size, shape and lustre, they are ready for the wholesale market. Some will be sold this way, and some will be retained. For example, the Mikimoto company uses only pearls which come from its own farms for its retail outlets, and sells no pearls to others.

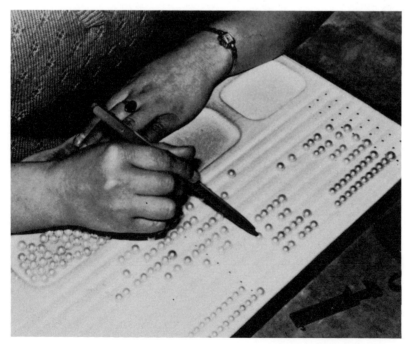

Assembling a pearl necklace is a task to try the patience of even an expert. The most highly skilled workers cannot assemble more than six strands in a day.

Each pearl is marked with a tiny dot for drilling. If the pearl has a slight imperfection, the dot is placed on that spot so that after drilling the pearl will be "perfect." The drill must pass exactly through the middle of the pearl so it will hang properly when strung.

WHOLESALE SALES

In 1957 the Ministry of International Trade and Industry of Japan enacted an ordinance "prohibiting the export from Japan of any but high-quality pearls." This development resulted from the combined efforts of the pearl cultivators, especially Kokichi Mikimoto, over a period of many years. The ordinance was a kind of insurance against irresponsible members of the pearl industry, who might have been tempted to "pass" pearls of inferior quality on to the unsuspecting public. Together with other pearl cultivators of integrity, the "Pearl King" waged a difficult campaign to maintain rigid standards for the cultured pearls to be placed on the market. On one occasion, Mikimoto bought inferior pearls worth thousands and burned them in the public square at the port city of Kobe. His extravagant gesture was effective in two ways: the inferior pearls were destroyed, and the resulting publicity dramatized the good faith of responsible Japanese pearl cultivators.

Offers for a "lot" of pearls at the auctions are submitted as sealed bids. The seller has the choice of accepting the highest bid or refusing the offer if the bids fall below his expectations. In this way, supply and demand set the price for cultured pearls.

Every phase of the cultured pearl industry is guided by associations which serve to regulate and promote the industry. Here, some of the leading cultured pearl exporters attend one of their regular monthly meetings.

In the years when the cultured pearl was not understood by the public, the industry suffered many setbacks in the export market. Controversies in England and France as to the value and worth of the cultured pearl resulted in violent court battles, but the Japanese cultured pearl exporters were eventually able to explain just what the cultured pearl was and show that it was certainly not an imitation pearl, but just as "real" as a natural pearl. Gradually, cultured pearls became accepted throughout the world.

The 1957 ordinance requires that all pearls placed on the export market be government inspected and stamped. In this way both the consumer and the cultured pearl industry are protected from low-quality or questionable merchandise and unfair prices.

THE AUCTION

The pearls presented for sale at auction are inspected by an impartial committee of experts, who determine the minimum price of each lot of pearls. A sample of each lot is placed on a velvet-covered tray next to a small box with a slotted lid, on which the minimum selling price is indicated. Bids are slipped inside the slot.

The auction room is arranged so that the light is precisely the same in every part of the room. No light is allowed to shine directly on the pearls, lying exposed on snowy white cloths, and no artificial light at all is allowed. The buyers test the pearls for roundness by rolling them gently. An imperfectly round pearl will roll off to one side or stop at its defect.

The buyers are allowed ample time to examine each lot of pearls and write their bids. After all the bids are "in," the boxes are opened and the bids examined. The lots go to the highest bidder, but if no one has bid the minimum price, the pearls are returned to the cultivator unsold. This practice maintains stable wholesale prices.

Many cultivators buy as many pearls as they sell at auction. Small pearl farmers, in particular, specialize in producing only certain sizes of pearls, and they supplement their produce with purchases from other cultivators. In this way small businesses can avoid the financial burdens imposed by the extra years of waiting necessary to produce large pearls.

PREPARATION FOR RETAIL SALE AND EXPORT

The bulk of the pearls exported from Japan are strung in graduated strands for necklaces, a process which is by no means as simple as it sounds. It takes many highly-skilled workers to assemble a single pearl necklace in a delicate series of intricate stages.

Drilling

The pearls to be strung must first be drilled. Each pearl must be studied carefully, and marked with a tiny ink dot for the mechanical drill. If a pearl is slightly blemished, the drill mark is placed on the imperfect spot so that when the drill hole is made it will cut through the blemish and remove it. The result will be a perfect pearl.

This is a close-up view of a high-speed precision drill. The pearl is painstakingly placed so that first one drill and then the other will pass through the middle. Care must be taken so the soft pearl does not shatter from the heat of drilling.

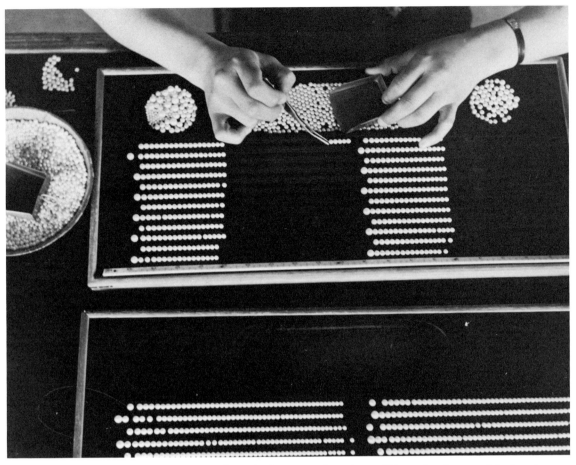

A strand of pearls must graduate gently from the large pearl in the middle to the clasp, and both sides must match perfectly. When the assembler finds two pearls which are alike in hue, shape, size and lustre, she places them one above the other in parallel grooves of the tray. This step is repeated until enough pearls have been assembled to complete the strand. Often the middle pearl is chosen last. Although here several necklaces are being assembled at one time, it may take several days to complete them all.

Drilling is the one phase of the industry which is dependent upon mechanical aid, but human assistance is much in evidence even here. Each pearl must be painstakingly hand-placed in the drill and clamped there. The tiny point of the drill must make its passage exactly through the middle of the pearl to produce straight and naturally hanging necklaces. Special care and handling are essential, for the pearl is so soft that it can crumble if carelessly drilled. Mechanical assembly-line production has no place in the production of cultured pearls.

Assembling

After drilling, experts must undertake the arduous task of assembling the necklaces. The drilled pearls are re-sorted according to size and hue and are placed in bowls on long tables

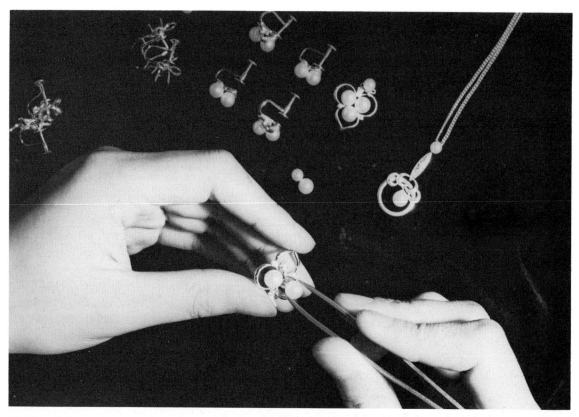

Half-drilled pearls are used in pins, rings, earrings and other pieces of manufactured jewelry. The pearl is carefully cemented on to a prong projecting from the surface of the metal.

in the sunny assembly room. To the average person, bowls of pearls are simply bowls of pearls, but the experts know that it may take as many as three bowls to yield one perfect necklace.

To achieve a perfect strand of pearls the gems must graduate gently and evenly in size from the large pearl in the middle of the strand to the small ones near the clasp. The pearls must match precisely in tint, lustre and shape, so the necklace will hang as one inseparable piece of jewelry when strung.

Black, grooved trays are used to assemble the strands. The expert selects pearls in steadily diminishing sizes and places them in the parallel grooves of her tray. Each groove represents one side of the necklace-to-be. When two pearls are matched they are placed in their proper sequence in the adjacent grooves. This parallel assembly assures that both sides of the necklace will be precisely the same. The process is so demanding that no more than six necklaces can be assembled by one person in a day.

Stringing

The pearls are then strung on silk thread with a very fine needle. (Nylon thread has a tendency to expand.) When the thread has been passed through all the pearls, the ends are knotted. The thread is not knotted between each pearl because it is believed this destroys the symmetry of the necklace by creating spaces between the so painstakingly-matched gems.

The necklace is then sent to the appraiser for final inspection and grading. Each necklace is inspected individually as to beauty and perfection of matching, and is then weighed and recorded. Sometimes 100 necklaces similar in quality are bound together for sale, and to see one of these huge clusters of gleaming pearls is to see an unforgettable vision of beauty.

LOOSE PEARLS

Pearls for brooches, earrings, cuff-links, rings and bracelets are not drilled, but sold as "loose" pearls. The majority of these pearls are mounted in the country where they are purchased, but many are sold in beautiful settings designed by Japanese artists.

After assembling, the necklaces are inspected and grouped according to length and quality.

DESTINATION: THE WORLD

An enormous quantity of cultured pearls from Japan is exported to overseas markets in the United States and Europe. These markets consume nearly 90 per cent of the total pearl crop each year, though markets in South America are expanding rapidly. The record export of $64,132,000 (£22,904,000) worth of pearls in 1965 surpassed the highest expectations of the pearl cultivators, and sales continue to increase steadily. The United States once bought the major percentage of the pearl harvest, but in recent years its share of the market has diminished as the demand for pearls has increased throughout the world. Great Britain, Italy, Switzerland, Hong Kong, India, Sweden, Brazil, France and West Germany are major importers.

To maintain these markets, every effort is being made to sustain the good reputation the cultured pearl industry has earned. The cultivators' associations, together with the Japanese Government, founded a strict quality control system to improve the products and services of the industry; in addition, these groups strive by their combined efforts to solve any problems which menace the industry, its workers, and the consumer.

As many as 3,000,000 strands of cultured pearl necklaces have been exported from Japan in a single year. Yet, this is far short of the goal of the "Pearl King," Mikimoto, who said he would like every woman in the world to have a cultured pearl necklace.

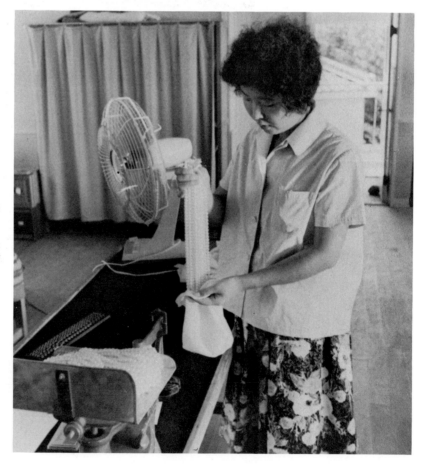

Weighing is the final step before the pearls are ready to be sold on the wholesale market. A group of necklaces of similar quality is often sold as a single unit.

Fine cultured pearls are available in more shapes, sizes, forms and prices than most people realize. Grouped round the cover of an antique incense burner are some of the varieties available in today's market. Prices are extremely varied: while the tear-shaped pearl dropped from the diamond-studded spray earring costs about $1,000 (£357) for the pearl alone, the 10 millimetre pearl on the lid costs only $75 (£27).

By-Products

SEED PEARLS

After the larger pearls of fine quality have been culled from the harvest, steps are taken to salvage the tiny "seed" pearls and pearl fragments which remain in the vats. The remains are transferred to a wooden or concrete macerating machine fitted with paddles. Sea water is added, and the whole mixture is churned into "settling" tanks. More than 99 per cent of the pearl material not previously removed is recovered in this way.

As the size of the pearl material collected by this method is very small, most of it is used for the manufacture of pearl medicine. However, the larger pearl fragments are separated, later to be used in the manufacture of costume jewelry or to decorate fine fabrics.

MEDICINES

Many people in the Orient believe that pearl and mother-of-pearl have great therapeutic value, and the demand for pearl medicine has always been high. With the development of

Rubies, diamonds and emeralds have been combined with lustrous baroque pearls to form these brooches. Valuable baroque pearls must have superior hue and lustre to compensate for their uneven shape.

the cultured pearl industry, Japan gained control of practically the entire pearl medicine market, and built a lucrative export trade on it.

Pearl medicine consists either of pulverized pearls or whole tiny seed pearls, and commands a high price. Since pearls contain a high percentage of calcium, doctors admit the finely ground pearl material probably has a slight beneficial effect, even if only as an antacid. At any rate, it is probably good for the teeth!

FERTILIZER AND OTHER PRODUCTS

At some farms, when facilities for cleaning and grinding are not available, the oyster shell is burned and made into quicklime. At other farms it is coarsely ground and bagged as calcium phosphate, fertilizer and chick feed. A small portion of the better shells are selected for jewelry, mother-of-pearl inlays, trinkets, buttons, and facings for collar-buttons, in addition to many other items.

CANNED PEARL OYSTERS

The ever-resourceful Mikimoto found a profitable way in which to utilize the adductor muscle of the harvested pearl oysters. Instead of throwing away those which the feasting harvesters were unable to consume, Mikimoto smoked and canned the adductor muscles in a plant he had specially built. The processing is similar to that used for smoking the common oyster.

Mikimoto used to give away tinned pearl oysters as complimentary gifts to his friends and business acquaintances. Today a number of companies are selling them.

Broome, on the tropical north coast of Western Australia, is famous for pearls and pearl shell. The splendid "Star of the West" pearl was found here in 1917. Pearling fleets fish the pearl beds from March to December, when the cyclone season begins. Each "lugger" like this carries a crew of 8 or 9 men, including 2 divers.

South Seas Pearls

The South Seas cultured pearl is, in general, very like the Japanese cultured pearl, as it, too, is the product of a living pearl oyster. The method of cultivating these pearls is nearly the same as in Japan. However, a different, much larger, breed of pearl oyster is used, and the resulting pearls are therefore two or three times larger than the Japanese pearls. If South Seas pearls are perfect, round and flawlessly white—though often they are not—they are very valuable.

The market for these large beauties is limited, for they are very costly. A single, flawless strand of round South Seas pearls costs as much as $150,000 (£50,000). But the South Seas

87

oysters do not yield as predictable a product as the Japanese oysters, and baroque pearls constitute the bulk of the harvest.

Moreover, it takes longer to produce the large gems. Hazards are increased, especially in Australia, by the long cyclone season when diving must be suspended. Political complications have made Burmese pearls almost impossible to obtain. So South Seas pearls represent a relatively small portion of the pearl industry, when compared with the Japanese production.

A limited quantity of cultured pearls is available each year from Australia. Much larger than Japanese cultured pearls, Australian pearls are very costly when perfect. Often, however, they are baroque.

Fresh-water pearl clams produce tiny, delicate pearls. This mollusc spent most of its life suspended in a plastic basket in the fresh waters of Lake Biwa, Japan, where most fresh-water pearls are produced (hence the name "Biwako" pearls).

Fresh-Water Pearls

Another very beautiful cultured jewel is the fresh-water "seed" pearl, sometimes called the Biwako pearl. These are tiny, irregularly shaped gems that make dainty, charming necklaces and bracelets. The fresh-water pearl is called a seed pearl because it is so small, but it bears no relation to a seed except as a convenience in description.

The history of the fresh-water cultured pearl in Japan goes back to 1928. Masayo Fujita, early associate and friend of Tokichi Nishikawa, was one of the first men to investigate fresh-water pearl culture. He was joined by several men from the Mikimoto staff in later years.

The results these scientists obtained, however, were considered unsatisfactory, and this section of the cultured pearl industry remained undeveloped for many years. Today the production of fresh-water cultured pearls represents only a fraction of that of the salt-water pearl, but the market is growing.

The waters of Lake Biwa are calm and peaceful except when motor boats patrol the area between the bamboo poles (rear).

The hub of the fresh-water cultured pearl industry is Biwa-ko, the largest fresh-water lake in Japan, which lies near Kyoto. The greenish-black fresh-water clams which produce the lustrous seed pearls are gathered by local fishermen from October to April. The clams are brought to special pens at the pearl farm to await the insertion operation. Some 75 per cent of the clams are gathered and operated upon during April, a time of feverish activity. Insertion operations are suspended, however, during June and July when the clams spawn.

Although the principle of the formation of a pearl sac is the basis for the production of fresh-water pearls, just as it is for salt-water cultured pearls, the practical details of its application are quite different.

When the fresh-water clams were first experimented upon, a serious problem developed: nearly half the clams died after a nucleus had been inserted. Even more catastrophic was the

Since fresh-water pearl clams are suspended at a depth of only 3 feet below the surface, their baskets need not be covered. As in Ago Bay, the baskets are suspended from bamboo rafts.

Biwako pearls are so small that they must be harvested carefully by hand, or some will be lost. Each oyster may produce more than 10 delicate jewels.

Squares of mantle tissue are used instead of pig-toe shell spheres as nuclei in fresh-water pearl clams. Several mantle grafts are inserted within each mollusc. Upon harvesting, each clam will yield a handful of dainty pearls.

This shipment of fresh-water pearls is valued at nearly $50,000 (£18,000). Each shipment is carefully inspected before it is exported.

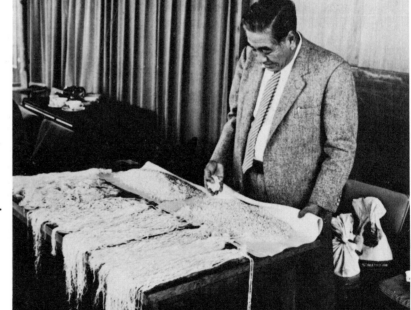

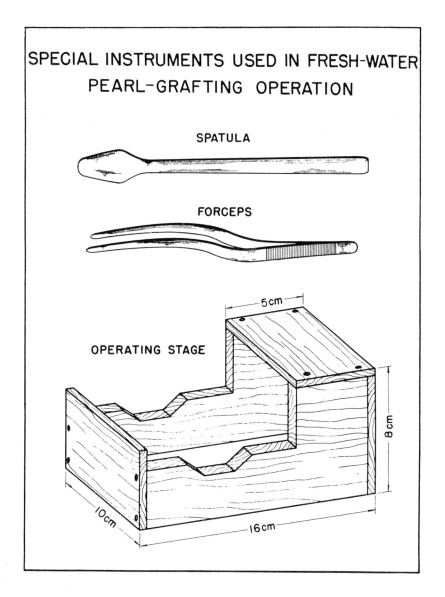

SPECIAL INSTRUMENTS USED IN FRESH-WATER
PEARL-GRAFTING OPERATION

SPATULA

FORCEPS

OPERATING STAGE

5cm

8cm

10cm

16cm

fact that those clams which did survive produced ugly, malformed pearls of no value at all. Investigation showed that *logic* was the cause of this unhappy development! Since the fresh-water clams were large, nuclei of large size had been inserted in hopes of obtaining large pearls. However, the anatomy of the big clam was discovered to be complicated by a long, twisting intestine, which interfered with the free depositing of nacre round the large nucleus. The introduction of large nuclei was soon abandoned and a new method was developed.

The clams are brought to the "operating" room and are pegged, just as the salt-water oysters are, as soon as they open their shells. The operator lifts the mantle of the clam gently with a special spatula, and cuts a small strip of tissue from the surface facing the clam's shell with a pair of razor-sharp scissors. This strip is placed on a wooden block, then carefully cleaned, and cut into tiny squares.

Securing the pegged clam in a clamp, the operator then delicately lifts the mantle from

Fresh-water pearls are so tiny that they must be tested after drilling to make sure the hole is perfect and that the drill has passed completely through.

the body which it protects, and inserts the tiny square grafts into the body of the clam, each square in a different place. Each clam can accommodate as many as ten grafts and still survive to produce pearls. The clam's body is not cut during the insertion process; a special forceps is used to push the grafts into the clam's body. And, most important, no nucleus is used: the graft tissue is the only "foreign" matter inserted.

Returned immediately to their retaining pens, the clams are left to their work for the next three years. Almost every introduced graft produces a tiny, elongated pearl, with amazingly lovely hue and lustre.

The meat of these clams is often eaten after the pearls are harvested, but it is reportedly quite tough and not very tasty. Although fresh-water pearls differ from salt-water cultured pearls in that they have no nucleus as such, both are true cultured pearls. Many Biwako pearls are made into delightful, delicate jewels or exported "loose" to countries round the world.

Assembling an attractive strand of the often baroque fresh-water pearls requires skill and a good sense of design.

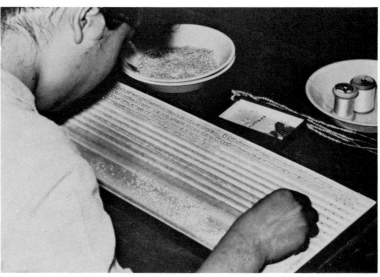

What seem to be only two or three different hues in a heap of pearls are actually as many as 12 shades. The visitor to a pearl farm is amazed to see how swiftly these workers are able to separate the various shades.

How to Care for Pearls

So much arduous work and painstaking care has gone into producing a single strand of lustrous pearls that it is almost an obligation of the purchaser to care for it properly. The pearl's very softness makes it vulnerable to damage, either by exposure to harsh substances or by knocking against hard objects. With proper handling, a strand of pearls can endure several generations, and be passed on from mother to daughter to be treasured and enjoyed.

The most frequent problem is loss of lustre. If pearls have not been worn for a long time they begin to look dull and lifeless. But their glow can be restored by gently rubbing a little olive oil and Tripoli (buffing) powder, mixed to a creamy consistency, over the pearls with a velvet cloth. After they are rinsed, the pearls must be dried carefully by patting with a soft cloth.

If the thread upon which they are strung becomes soiled, pearls can be soaked in a mild solution of soft soap and tepid water. To prevent damage to the pearls, the container in which they are soaked should be lined with a soft, fluffy towel. And the pearls must not be scrubbed! If a 10-minute soaking does not remove the dirt, the pearls may be rolled *gently* over the towel lining the container. A thorough rinsing and a delicate polishing with pure olive oil will restore their lustre.

In between wearings, pearls should be kept between layers of cotton or velvet in a covered box, so they will not become scratched.

INDEX